Lyrics & Chords

Over **80** Massive Anthems

Published by
WISE PUBLICATIONS
14-15 Berners Street, London W1T 3LJ, UK.

Exclusive Distributors:
MUSIC SALES LIMITED
Distribution Centre, Newmarket Road,
Bury St Edmunds, Suffolk IP33 3YB, UK.
MUSIC SALES PTY LIMITED
Music Sales Pty Limited
20 Resolution Drive, Caringbah, NSW 2229, Australia.

Order No. AM1001374
ISBN 978-1-84938-663-0
This book © Copyright 2010 Wise Publications,
a division of Music Sales Limited.

Music arranged by Matt Cowe.
Music edited by Adrian Hopkins.
Compiled by Nick Crispin.
Music processed by Paul Ewers Music Design.

Cover photo courtesy of Simone Joyner/Getty Images.
Photo page 214 courtesy of Andy Sheppard/Getty Images.
All other photos courtesy of LFI.

Printed in the EU.

Your Guarantee of Quality
As publishers, we strive to produce every book to the
highest commercial standards. This book has been carefully
designed to minimise awkward page turns and to make
playing from it a real pleasure. Particular care has been
given to specifying acid-free, neutral-sized paper made from pulps
which have not been elemental chlorine bleached. This pulp is from
farmed sustainable forests and was produced with special regard
for the environment. Throughout, the printing and binding have
been planned to ensure a sturdy, attractive publication which
should give years of enjoyment. If your copy fails to meet our high
standards, please inform us and we will gladly replace it.

www.musicsales.com

WISE PUBLICATIONS
PART OF THE MUSIC SALES GROUP
LONDON / NEW YORK / PARIS / SYDNEY / COPENHAGEN / BERLIN / MADRID / TOKYO

Contents

Acts Of Man

Words & Music by
Tim Smith

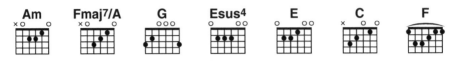

Capo third fret

Intro ‖: Am | Fmaj7/A | G | Esus4 E :‖

Verse 1

Am   Fmaj7/A   G   Esus4 E
 If all that grows starts to fade, starts to fal - ter,

Am   Fmaj7/A   G   Esus4 E
Oh, let me in - side, let me in - side, not to wake.

Am   Fmaj7/A   G   Esus4 E
Let all that run through the fields through the qui - et

Am   Fmaj7/A   G   Esus4 E
Go on with their own, on with their own hidden ways.

Link 1 ‖: Am | Fmaj7/A | G | Esus4 E :‖

Verse 2

Am   Fmaj7/A G   Esus4 E
 When all newness of gold travels far from

Am   Fmaj7/A   G   Esus4 E
Where it had once been, worn like the earth over years.

 Am   Fmaj7/A   G   Esus4 E
And when the acts of men cause the ground to break op - en,

Am   Fmaj7/A   G   Esus4 E
Oh, let me in - side, let me in - side, not to wake.

Chorus 1

```
Am          F      G     C
Great are the sounds of all that live
     F             E
And all that man can hold.
```

Instrumental

```
‖: Am      | F       | G        | C        |
   | F      | F       | E        :‖
```

Verse 3

```
Am         Fmaj7/A       G              Esus4  E
   If all that grows starts to fade, starts to fal  -  ter,
Am              Fmaj7/A        G          Esus4    E
Oh, let me in - side, let me in - side, not to wake.
```

Chorus 2

```
Am          F      G     C
Great are the sounds of all that live
     F             E
And all that man can hold.
Am          F      G     C        F    E  Am
Great are the sounds of all that live, that live.
```

Animal

Words & Music by
Christian Karlsson, Pontus Winnberg,
Andrew Wyatt & Henrik Jonback

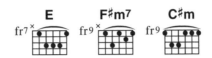

Intro ‖: E | F#m7 | C#m | C#m :‖

Verse 1

E   F#m7
There was a time when my world was filled with

 C#m
Da - rkness, darkness darkness.

E   F#m7
Then I stopped dreaming, now I'm supposed to fill it up with

 C#m
So - mething, something, something.

E   F#m7   C#m
 In your eyes I see the eyes of somebody I knew be - fore,

Long long, long ago.

E   F#m7
 But I'm still trying to make my mind up,

C#m
 Am I free or am I tied up?

Chorus 1

E   F#m7
I change shapes just to hide in this place,

  C#m
But I'm still, I'm still an animal.

E   F#m7
Nobody knows it but me when I slip,

  C#m
Yeah I slip, I'm still an animal.

Verse 2

E   F♯m7
There is a hole and I tried to fill it up with

      C♯m
Mo - ney, money, money.

E   F♯m7
But it gets bigger till your horse is always

      C♯m
Run - ning, running, running.

E   F♯m7   C♯m
In your eyes I see the eyes of somebody who could be strong,

Tell me if I'm wrong.

E   F♯m7
And now I'm pulling your dis - guise up.

C♯m
Are you free or are you tied up?

Chorus 2

E   F♯m7
I change shapes just to hide in this place,

      C♯m
But I'm still, I'm still an animal.

E   F♯m7
Nobody knows it but me when I slip,

      C♯m
Yeah I slip, I'm still an animal.

E   F♯m7
I change shapes just to hide in this place,

      C♯m
But I'm still, I'm still an animal.

E   F♯m7
Nobody knows it but me when I slip,

      C♯m
Yeah I slip, I'm still an animal.

Link 1   ‖: E | F♯m7 | C♯m | C♯m :‖

Instrumental ‖: E | F♯m7 | C♯m | C♯m :‖ *Play 6 times*

Chorus 3   As Chorus 2

Outro   ‖: E | F♯m7 | C♯m | C♯m :‖ *Play 4 times*

Jónsi

Animal Arithmetic

Words & Music by
Jón Birgisson

E	A	B	E/G♯	D/F♯	D	A/C♯

Capo first fret

Intro ‖ E | E | E | E ‖

Verse 1

E
Wake up, cut my hair, making food disappear,

A
Riding bikes, making out, elephants run you down.

E
You and I run away, blushing cheeks,

                  A
Howling wolves, colourful fireworks.

                                    E   B
Every time, everyone, everything's full of life,

A   E   B
Everyday, everywhere, people are so a - live.

Chorus 1

(B)   E/G♯ A   E   B
We should all be, oh, a - live.

              E/G♯ A   E   B
We should all be, oh, a - live.

Link 1 ‖ A | A | D | D ‖

Verse 2

A
Horfandi, þegjandi, tala við, skríðandi

D/F♯
Dreymandi, strjúka af, koma við ekki má

A
Mála á líkama, spilað á renglandi

D/F♯
Hlaupandi! Leikandi!

D   A   E
Get it on, let it out, fucking and spúan - di.

D   A   E
Get it on, let it out, fucking and kæfan - di.

Chorus 2

(E)   A/C♯ D   A   E
We should all be, oh, a - live.

       A/C♯ D   A   E
Exist all in love, in life.

       A/C♯ D   A   E
We should all be, oh, a - live.

       A/C♯   D   A   (E)
Let's not stop, let's grow and live.

Bridge 1

N.C.(E)
I see you colourful, I see you in the trees,

I see you spiritful, you're in the breeze.

I see it in your hands, tree fingers draw a beam,

I see you in the sand, roll down the stream.

E   E/G♯   A   B
  I see you in the trees,   I see you colourful,

E/G♯   A   E/G♯   B
  I see you in the breeze,   you're spirit - ful.

E   E/G♯   A   B
  Tree fingers draw a beam,   I see it in your hands,

E/G♯   A   E/G♯   B
  You're rolling down the stream,   you're in the sand.

Bridge 2

E   E/G♯   A   B
I see you colourful,   I see you in the trees,

E/G♯   A   E/G♯   B
I see you spiritful,   you're in the breeze.

E   E/G♯   A   B
I see it in your hands,   tree fingers draw a beam,

E/G♯   A   E/G♯   B
I see you in the sand,   roll down the stream.

E   E/G♯   A   B
I see you in the trees,   I see you colourful,

E/G♯   A   E/G♯   B
I see you in the breeze,   you're spirit - ful.

E   E/G♯   A   B
Tree fingers draw a beam,   I see it in your hands,

E/G♯   A   E/G♯   B
You're rolling down the stream,   you're in the sand.

E   E/G♯   A   B
I see you colourful,   I see you in the trees,

E/G♯   A   E/G♯   B
I see you spiritful,   you're in the breeze.

E   E/G♯   A   B
I see it in your hands,   tree fingers draw a beam,

E/G♯   A   E/G♯   B   E
I see you in the sand,   roll down the stream.

Ambling Alp

Words & Music by
Christopher Keating, Anand Wilder & Ira Wolf Tuton

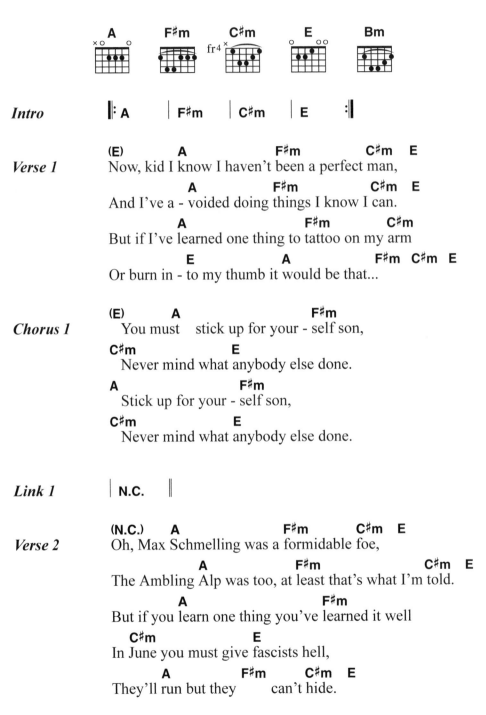

Intro

‖: A | F♯m | C♯m | E :‖

Verse 1

(E)   A   F♯m   C♯m E
Now, kid I know I haven't been a perfect man,
               A   F♯m   C♯m E
And I've a - voided doing things I know I can.
           A   F♯m   C♯m
But if I've learned one thing to tattoo on my arm
         E   A   F♯m C♯m E
Or burn in - to my thumb it would be that...

Chorus 1

(E)   A   F♯m
  You must   stick up for your - self son,
C♯m   E
  Never mind what anybody else done.
A   F♯m
  Stick up for your - self son,
C♯m   E
  Never mind what anybody else done.

Link 1

| N.C. ‖

Verse 2

(N.C.)   A   F♯m   C♯m E
Oh, Max Schmelling was a formidable foe,
            A   F♯m   C♯m E
The Ambling Alp was too, at least that's what I'm told.
           A   F♯m
But if you learn one thing you've learned it well
       C♯m   E
In June you must give fascists hell,
        A   F♯m   C♯m E
They'll run but they   can't hide.

Chorus 2

(E)   A   F♯m
You must   stick up for your - self son,

C♯m   E
Never mind what anybody else done.

A   F♯m
Stick up for your - self son,

C♯m   E
Never mind what anybody else done.

A   F♯m
Stick up for your - self son,

C♯m   E
Never mind what anybody else done.

A   F♯m
Stick up for your - self son,

C♯m   E
Never mind what anybody else done.

Bridge

Bm   F♯m
And when those thunder clouds are crying

       A   E
In the skies, in the skies.

Bm   F♯m
And when those fireflies keep shining

       A   E
In your eyes, in your eyes.

Bm
Keep your mind on the time,

F♯m
With your ass on the line,

Bm   F♯m A   E
Keep your fleet feet sliding side to the side.

Verse 3

(E)   A   F♯m   C♯m   E
Now the world can be an unfair place at times,

      A   F♯m   C♯m E
But your lows will have their complement of highs.

      A   F♯m   C♯m   E
And if anyone should cheat you, take ad - vantage of or beat you,

      A   F♯m   C♯m   E
Raise your head and   wear your wounds with pride.

Chorus 3   As Chorus 2

Outro   ‖: A | F♯m | C♯m | E   :‖ A   ‖

Airplanes

Words & Music by
Taylor Rice, Kelcey Ayer,
Andrew Hamm, Ryan Hahn & Matthew Frazier

D	A/C#	Bm	D/A	A	A7

Intro ‖: D │ D │ A/C# │ Bm D/A │

│ Bm D/A │ A A7 :‖

Verse 1

D   A/C#
   The desk where you sit in - side of a frame
Bm D/A   Bm D/A   A   A7
Made of,   made of,   of wood.
D   A/C#
   I keep those chopsticks you had from when you
Bm   D/A   Bm D/A   A   A7
Taught a - broad,   taught a - broad   in Ja - pan.

Chorus 1

(A7)   D
I love it all
A/C#
So much I call
Bm D/A Bm D/A   A   A7
I want you back, back, back,   you back.

Verse 2

D   A/C#
   I did not know you as well as my
Bm D/A   Bm D/A   A   A7
Fath - er,   fath - er   knew you.
D   A/C#
   Every question you took the time to sit and
Bm D/A   Bm D/A   A   A7
Look it up,   look it up,   encyclo - pedia.

Chorus 2

   (A7)   **D**
I love it all
            A/C♯
So much I call
         Bm **D/A** **Bm** **D/A**   **A**   **A7**
I want you back, back, back,   you back.
            D
I love it all
            A/C♯
So much I call
         Bm **D/A** **Bm** **D/A**   **A**   **A7**
I want you back, back, back,   you back, hey.

Instrumental | **D** | **D** | **A/C♯** | **Bm** **D/A** |

            | **Bm** **D/A** | **A** **A7** |

Verse 3

D   **A/C♯**
  It sounds like we would of had a great deal
   Bm **D/A**   **Bm** **D/A**   **A**   **A7**
To say,   to say   to each other.
D   **A/C♯**
  I bet when I leave my bo - dy for the sky,
   Bm **D/A**   **Bm** **D/A**   **A**   **A7**
The wait,   the wait   will be worth it.

Chorus 3

   (A7)   **D**
I love it all
            A/C♯
So much I call
         Bm **D/A** **Bm** **D/A**   **A**   **A7**
I want you back, back, back,   you back.
            D
I love it all
            A/C♯
So much I call
         Bm **D/A** **Bm** **D/A**   **A**
I want you back, back, back,   you back,
   A7 **D** **A/C♯** **Bm** **D/A** **Bm** **D/A**
Hey._____
   A **A7** **D** **N.C.**
Oh._____

Airplanes

Words & Music by
Bobby Ray Simmons Jr., Tim Sommers,
Jeremy Dussolliet, Alexander Grant & Justin Franks

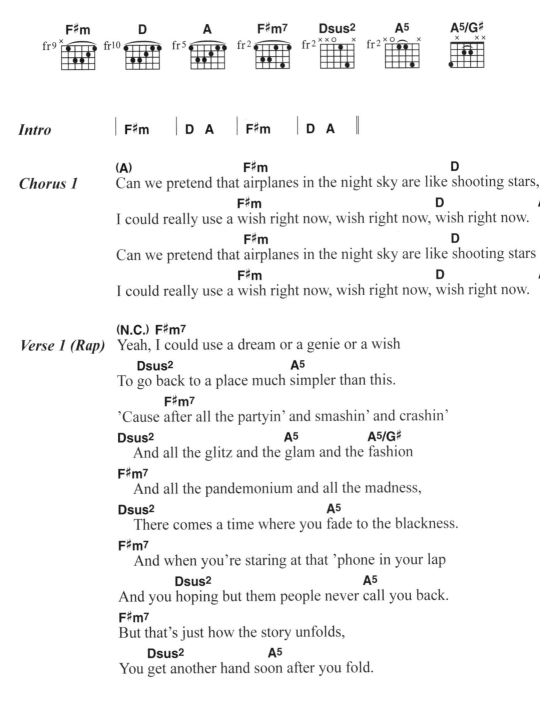

F#m   D   A   F#m7   Dsus2   A5   A5/G#

Intro | F#m | D A | F#m | D A ‖

Chorus 1
(A)   F#m   D   A
Can we pretend that airplanes in the night sky are like shooting stars,
                    F#m   D   A
I could really use a wish right now, wish right now, wish right now.
                    F#m   D   A
Can we pretend that airplanes in the night sky are like shooting stars
                    F#m   D   A
I could really use a wish right now, wish right now, wish right now.

Verse 1 (Rap)
(N.C.) F#m7
Yeah, I could use a dream or a genie or a wish
      Dsus2   A5
To go back to a place much simpler than this.
          F#m7
'Cause after all the partyin' and smashin' and crashin'
Dsus2   A5   A5/G#
   And all the glitz and the glam and the fashion
F#m7
   And all the pandemonium and all the madness,
Dsus2   A5
   There comes a time where you fade to the blackness.
F#m7
   And when you're staring at that 'phone in your lap
      Dsus2   A5
And you hoping but them people never call you back.
F#m7
But that's just how the story unfolds,
      Dsus2   A5
You get another hand soon after you fold.

cont.

F#m7
And when your plans unravel
                 Dsus2   A5   A5/G#
And they sayin' what would you wish for if you had one chance?
    F#m7
So airplane, airplane sorry I'm late,
     Dsus2   A5
I'm on my way so don't close that gate,
    F#m7
If I don't make that then I'll switch my flight
        Dsus2   A5
And I'll be right back at it by the end of the night.

Chorus 2   As Chorus 1

    (A)   F#m7
Verse 2 (Rap) Yeah, yeah, somebody take me back to the days
           Dsus2   A5
Before this was a job, before I got paid,
        F#m7
Before it ever mattered what I had in my bank.
           Dsus2   A5
Yeah, back when I was tryin' to get a tip at Subway
   A5/G#   F#m7
And back when I was rappin' for the hell of it,
        Dsus2   A5
But nowadays we rappin' to stay relevant.
            F#m7
I'm guessin' that if we can make some wishes outta airplanes,
        Dsus2   A5
Then maybe yo maybe I'll go back to the days
   A5/G#   F#m7
Be - fore the poli - tics that we call the rap game,
        Dsus2   A5
And back when ain't nobody listened to my mix tape
        F#m7
And back before I tried to cover up my slang.
        Dsus2   A5
But this is for De - catur, what's up Bobby Ray,
   A5/G#   F#m7
So can I get a wish to end the politics
        Dsus2   A5
And get back to the music that started this shit.
    F#m7
So here I stand and then again I say,
           N.C.
I'm hopin' we can make some wishes outta airplanes.

Chorus 3   As Chorus 1

Outro

F♯m7   Dsus2 A5
   I could really use a wish right now,

  F♯m   Dsus2 A5
I, I,   I could really use a wish right now.

      F♯m7   Dsus2
Like, like,   like shooting stars,

A5   F♯m7   Dsus2 A5
I, I, I,   I could really use a wish right now

      A5/G♯   N.C.
A wish, a wish right now.

The Cave

Words & Music by
Marcus Mumford

C#m7   E/B   G#5   E   A(add9)/E   B   C#m7*   A

Capo second fret

⑥ = D   ③ = F#
⑤ = A   ② = A
④ = D   ① = D

Intro

| C#m7 | E/B | C#m7 | E/B |

| C#m7 | E/B G#5 | E A(add9)/E | E |

Verse 1

(E)   C#m7   E/B
It's empty in the valley of your heart,

      C#m7   E/B
The sun, it rises slowly as you walk

      C#m7
Away from all the fears

    E/B   G#5   E   A(add9)/E E
And all the faults you've left be - hind.

      C#m7   E/B
The harvest left no food for you to eat,

      C#m7   E/B
You cannibal, you meat-eater, you see.

      C#m7
But I have seen the same,

   E/B   G#5   E   A(add9)/E E
I know the shame in your de - feat.

Chorus 1

E   A(add9)/E E
But I will hold on   hope

    A(add9)/E E
And I won't let you   choke

A(add9)/E E   B
On the noose a - round your neck.

cont.

    C♯m⁷   A   E
And I'll find strength in pain

    C♯m⁷ A   E
And I will change my ways,

      A   E   B
I'll know my name as it's called again.

Link 1

| C♯m⁷ | E/B | C♯m⁷ | E/B | |

| C♯m⁷ | E/B G♯5 | E A(add9)/E E | ‖

Verse 2

(E)   C♯m⁷   E/B
'Cause I have other things to fill my time,

           C♯m⁷   E/B
You take what is yours and I'll take mine.

           C♯m⁷
Now let me at the truth

          E/B   G♯5   E   A(add9)/E E
Which will re - fresh my broken mind.

        C♯m⁷   E/B
So tie me to a post and block my ears,

           C♯m⁷   E/B
I can see widows and orphans through my tears.

         C♯m⁷
I know my call de - spite my faults

    E/B   G♯5   E   A(add9)/E E
And de - spite my growing fears.

Chorus 2   As Chorus 1

Verse 3

(E)   C♯m⁷   E/B
So come out of your cave walking on your hands

           C♯m⁷   E/B
And see the world hanging upside down.

           C♯m⁷
You can understand de - pendence

    E/B   G♯5   E   A(add9)/E E
When you know the maker's land.

Chorus 3

    E   A(add9)/E E
So make your siren's   call

       E   A(add9)/E E
And sing all you   want,

    A(add9)/E E   B
I will not   hear what you have to say.

       C♯m7* A   E
'Cause I need freedom now

       C♯m7* A   E
And I need to know how

     A   E   B
To live my life as it's meant to be.

Instrumental ‖: E | A E | E | A E | A E | B   :‖

Chorus 4

    E   A(add9)/E E
And I will hold on   hope

           A(add9)/E E
And I won't let you   choke

A(add9)/E E   B
On   the   noose a - round your neck.

     C♯m7* A   E
And I'll find strength in pain

     C♯m7* A   E
And I will   change my ways,

     A   E   B   E
I'll know my name as it's called again.

Biffy Clyro

The Captain

Words by Simon Neil
Music by Biffy Clyro

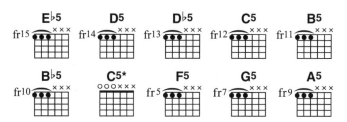

⑥ = C   ③ = F
⑤ = G   ② = A
④ = C   ① = D

Intro

| Eb5 D5 Db5 C5 B5 Bb5 C5* |

| C5 C5* C5 C5* C5 C5* Eb5 | C5 C5* C5 C5* C5 C5*   Eb5 D5 Db5 |

| C5 C5* C5 C5* C5 C5* Eb5 | C5 C5* C5 C5* Eb5 D5 Db C5 B5 Bb5 |

| C5* | F5 G5 ‖

Verse 1

C5*
    Angels fall to the floor,
       F5   G5
Like they would if I was captain.
C5*
    "Silver children," she roared,
    F5   G5
"I'm not the son of God."
C5*
Somebody help me sing,
    F5   G5
Can anybody hear me?
C5*
Liars and lovers combine tonight,
     F5   G5
We're gonna make a scene.

Pre-chorus 1

A5   **F5**   **C5***   **G5**
Somebody help me sing, whoa, oh, oh.
A5   **F5**   **C5***   **G5**
Somebody help me sing, whoa, oh, oh.

Chorus 1

C5*
Help me be captain of
G5
    Our crippled disguises.
   A5
I won't show what's underneath,
G5
    It's time for surprises.
   C5*
I can't climb up your ladder,
G5
I can't ride your horse,
     A5
I've swallowed half an hourglass,
   G5
So now the landscape is swollen up.

Link 1

| **C5*** | **F5** | **C5*** | **F5** | ‖ |

Verse 2

C5*
   I gave birth to a fire,
   F5   **G5**
It's like it's features were burning.
C5*   **F5**   **G5**
   I'm in control, I am the son of God.
C5*
Somebody help me sing,
    F5   **G5**
Can anybody hear me?
C5*
Line up your soldiers one final time,
    F5   **G5**
We're gonna have a ball.

Pre-chorus 2   As Pre-chorus 1

Chorus 2   As Chorus 1

Link 2 | C5* | G5 | A5 | G5   F5 |

Bridge

C5*
Let's throw death away.
G5
Let's throw death away.
A5
Let's throw death away.
G5   **F5**
Let's throw death away.
C5*
Let's throw death away.
G5
Let's throw death away.
A5
Let's throw death away.
G5   **F5**
Let's throw death away.

Outro | C5 C5* C5 C5* C5 C5* E♭5 | C5 C5* C5 C5* C5 C5*   E♭5 D5 D♭5 |

| C5 C5* C5 C5* C5 C5* E♭5 | C5 C5* C5 C5* C5 C5* E♭5 ‖

Best Friend

Words & Music by
Jonny Pierce & Jacob Graham

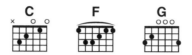

Intro

‖: C | F | C | F G :‖

Verse 1

    C   F   C
You're my best friend,   but then you died

           F   G   C
When I was twenty three and you were twenty five.

           F   C   F
You're my best friend, but then you died,

    G   C   F   C F
And how will I sur - vive, survive, sur - vive, survive?

  G   C   F   C F G
Oh, how will I sur - vive, survive, sur - vive, survive?

Chorus 1

(G)   C   F
And every day I waited for you,

         C   F   G
And every day on the top of your car.

       C   F
Every day I waited for you,

         C   F   G
And every day on the hood of your car.

Link 1

C F C F G
Ah, ah, ah, ah, ho, oh.

C F C F G
Ah, ah, ah, ah, ho, oh.

Link 2

C   F   C   F G
Ho, ho, ho, oh, ho, ho.

C   F   C   F G
Ho, ho, ho, oh, ho, oh.

Verse 2

C   F   C
I had a dream of you,   you were drifting a - way,

        F   G   C
You were sad, you always would drift a - way.

        F   C
And I know you're going to be o - kay,

F   G   C   F   C
'Cause I can see it in your eyes, your eyes, your eyes, your eyes,

F   G   C   F   C F G
And I know I wanna sur - vive, survive, sur - vive, survive.

Chorus 2   As Chorus 1

Link 3   As Link 1

Instrumental ‖: C | F | C | F G :‖

Link 4   As Link 2

Chorus 3   As Chorus 1

Outro

       C F C F   G
Ah, ah, ah, ah, ho, oh.

       C F C F   G
Ah, ah, ah, ah, ho, oh.

       C F C F   G
Ah, ah, ah, ah, ho, oh.

       C F C F   G C
Ah, ah, ah, ah, ho, oh.

Black & Blue

Words & Music by
Christian Karlsson, Pontus Winnberg, Henrik Jonback,
Andrew Wyatt & Juliet Richardson

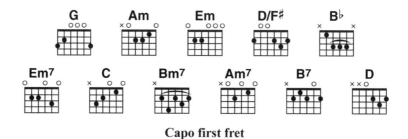

Capo first fret

Intro

| G | | G Am | Em | | Em D/F♯ ||

Verse 1

G   Am Em   Em   D/F♯ G
How long has it   been, shall we get into it a - gain?

          Am Em   G
Excuse, our dis - grace, we've had no time to paint the place,

         B♭   Em
The dog is al - ways barking at the mailman.

Pre-chorus 1

G   Am   Em
I won't waste your time with my re - vela - tion.

Chorus 1

Em7 C   Bm7   Em7
     Hello my friend, I see you're back a - gain.

C   Bm7   Am7
Hello mystery, don't bother to ex - plain.

Em7 C   Bm7   Em7
     How 'bout maybe, it's all been in my head.

C   Bm7   B7   G
Hey world I'm tired of this black and blue, black and blue.

Verse 2

```
G                   Am  Em                              D/F♯  G
My dear, come a - gain, your voice is fading out and    in,
            Am      Em                        D/F♯  G
Out of the laundry bin, I found my innocence a  -  gain.
                    B♭    Em
The dog is al - ways barking at the mailman.
```

Pre-chorus 2   As Pre-chorus 1

Chorus 2   As Chorus 1

Instrumental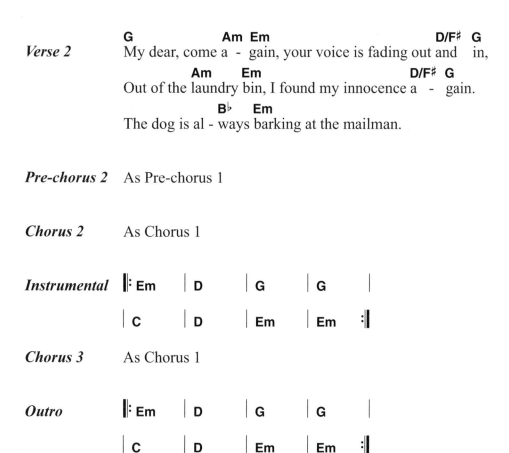

Em │ D │ G │ G │

C │ D │ Em │ Em

Chorus 3   As Chorus 1

Outro   Em │ D │ G │ G │

C │ D │ Em │ Em

Bloodbuzz Ohio

Words & Music by
Matt Berninger, Aaron Dessner & Padma Newsome

Intro | N.C. | N.C. | N.C. | N.C. |

| F#m7 | F#m7 | F#m7 | F#m7 ‖

Verse 1

A
    Stand up straight at the foot of your love,

F#m
I   lift my shirt up.

A
    Stand up straight at the foot of your love,

F#m
I   lift my shirt up.

    A   F#m
I was carried to Ohio in a swarm of bees,

           A   A/C#   F#m
I'll never marry, but O - hio don't remember me.

Verse 2

A
    Lay my head on the hood of your car,

F#m
I   take it too far.

A
    Lay my head on the hood of your car,

F#m
I   take it too far.

Bridge 1

(F♯m)   D   D/F♯

I still owe money to the money, to the money I owe,

          A   A/C♯

I never thought about love when I thought about home.

             D   D/F♯

I still owe money to the money, to the money I owe,

             A   A/C♯

The floors are falling out from every - body I know.

Chorus 1

(A/C♯)   D

I'm on a blood buzz,

D/F♯   D/E

Yes I am.

            A   A/C♯

I'm on a blood buzz.

            D

I'm on a blood buzz,

D/F♯   D/E

God I am,

            A

I'm on a blood buzz.

Link 1

| A | A | A | A | |

| F♯m | F♯m | F♯m | F♯m |

Verse 3

(F♯m) A   F♯m

I was carried to Ohio in a swarm of bees,

            A   F♯m

I'll never marry, but Ohio don't remember me.

Bridge 2   As Bridge 1

Chorus 2   As Chorus 1

Outro

‖: A | A | A | A | |

| F♯m | F♯m | F♯m | F♯m :‖

| A | A | A | A | A | ‖

Born Again

Words & Music by
Richard Ashcroft, Ernest Wilson & Kevin Randolph

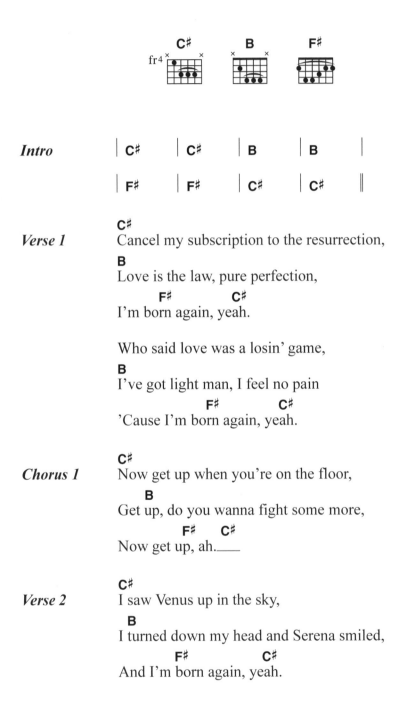

Intro
| C♯ | C♯ | B | B |

| F♯ | F♯ | C♯ | C♯ ‖

Verse 1

C♯
Cancel my subscription to the resurrection,

B
Love is the law, pure perfection,

    F♯   **C♯**
I'm born again, yeah.

Who said love was a losin' game,

B
I've got light man, I feel no pain

     F♯   **C♯**
'Cause I'm born again, yeah.

Chorus 1

C♯
Now get up when you're on the floor,

   B
Get up, do you wanna fight some more,

    F♯ **C♯**
Now get up, ah.___

Verse 2

C♯
I saw Venus up in the sky,

   B
I turned down my head and Serena smiled,

   F♯   **C♯**
And I'm born again, yeah.

cont. I held the hand of a crying girl,

B
Brooklyn tears yeah, I've felt the spell,

      F♯   **C♯**
I was born again, yeah.

Chorus 2
    C♯
Now get up when you're on the floor,

    B   **F♯** **C♯**
Get up, do you wanna fight some more, now get up, ah.___

                               B
This is life in the end you know that it's light

                       F♯   **C♯**
There's no need to cry through the night, ah.___

Verse 3
    C♯
Now I'm a man who ain't afraid,

    B
I de - stroyed my ego just to make the space,

        F♯   **C♯**
'Cause I'm born again, yeah.

And when I feel a melody,

    B
I get a righteous charge right through me,

        F♯   **C♯**
Yeah I'm born again, yeah.

Chorus 3
    C♯
Now get up when you're on the floor,

        B
Just get up, don't wanna fight no more,

        F♯ **C♯**
Now get up, ah.___

                                          B
'Cause that's life and in the end you know that it's light,

                       F♯   **C♯**
There's no need to cry through the night, ah.___

Outro
    C♯
All together now,

        B   **F♯**
Na, na, na, na, na, na, na, na, na.

        C♯
Come on,   one life, one life, let's go

  ‖: **C♯**   **B**   **F♯** **C♯**
‖: Na, na, na, na, na, na, na, na, na.   :‖

      Repeat to fade (with ad lib. vocals)

Celestica

Words & Music by
Ethan Kath & Alice Glass

F#m	Em6	Bm	D	A	Em

Intro ‖: F#m | Em6 | Bm | Bm :‖ *Play 4 times*

Verse 1

(Bm) F#m   Em6   Bm
As we fall into sequence   and we're eating our young,

　　　　　D　　　　　A　　　Bm
Remain silent and still for   modes - ty.

　　　　　F#m   Em6   Bm
When the splints have been broken   and they can't help you no

　　　　　D　　　　A　　　　Bm
Do you pray with your eyes   closed natural - ly?

Chorus 1

F#m   Em6   Bm
Follow me into   no - where,

D   A   Bm
Woven with   the utmost care.

Verse 2

(Bm) F#m   Em6   Bm
If I'm lost please don't find me,   if I jump let me sink.

　　　　　D　　　　　A　　　　Bm
We des - cended from no   one with a wink.

Link 1 | N.C. | N.C. | N.C. | N.C. ‖

Bridge 1

    D   F♯m   Em
    When it's cold outside hold me, don't hold me.
    D   F♯m   Em
When I choose to rest my eyes coax me, don't coax me.
    D   F♯m   Em
    When it's cold outside hold me, don't hold me.
    D   F♯m   Em
When I choose to rest my eyes coax me, don't coax me.

Link 2

| Bm | Bm |

| F♯m | Em6 | Bm | Bm |

| D | A | Bm | Bm   ‖

Chorus 2

F♯m   Em6   Bm
Follow me   into no - where,
D   A   Bm
Woven with   the utmost care.

Verse 3

(Bm)   F♯m   Em6   Bm
Have they cleansed you with chloride   and scrubbed behind the knees?
                  D   A   Bm
Has your body been   hollowed by the breeze?

Outro

| F♯m | Em6 | Bm | Bm |

| D | A | Bm | Bm |

| N.C. | N.C. | N.C. | N.C.   ‖

‖: F♯m | Em6 | Bm | Bm   :‖ *Play 4 times to fade*

Closer To The Edge

Words & Music by
Jared Leto

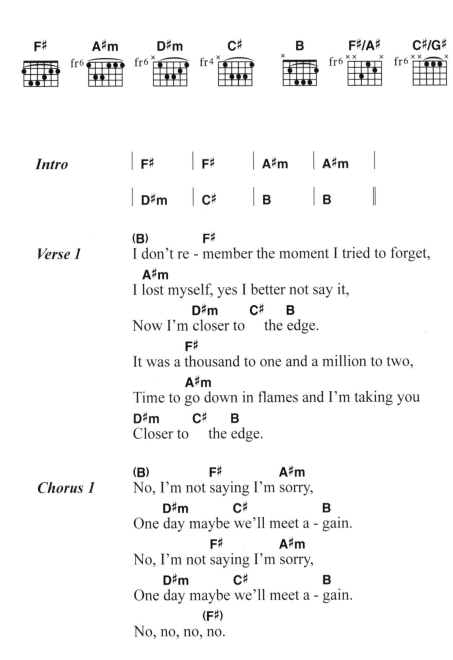

Intro

| F♯ | F♯ | A♯m | A♯m |

| D♯m | C♯ | B | B |

Verse 1

(B)   F♯
I don't re - member the moment I tried to forget,

A♯m
I lost myself, yes I better not say it,

D♯m   C♯   B
Now I'm closer to   the edge.

F♯
It was a thousand to one and a million to two,

A♯m
Time to go down in flames and I'm taking you

D♯m   C♯   B
Closer to   the edge.

Chorus 1

(B)   F♯   A♯m
No, I'm not saying I'm sorry,

D♯m   C♯   B
One day maybe we'll meet a - gain.

F♯   A♯m
No, I'm not saying I'm sorry,

D♯m   C♯   B
One day maybe we'll meet a - gain.

(F♯)
No, no, no, no.

Link | F♯ | F♯ | A♯m | A♯m |

| D♯m | C♯ | B | B ‖

Verse 2

  (B)   F♯
Can you i - magine a time when the truth ran free?

   A♯m
A birth of a song, the death of a dream,

D♯m   C♯   B
Closer to   the edge.

F♯   A♯m
   This never ending story,   keep forward driving fate,

D♯m   C♯   B
   We all fall short of glory, lost in ourselves.

Chorus 2

  (B)   F♯   A♯m
No, I'm not saying I'm sorry,

    D♯m   C♯   B
One day maybe we'll meet a - gain.

          F♯   A♯m
No, I'm not saying I'm sorry,

    D♯m   C♯   B
One day maybe we'll meet a - gain.

        (F♯/A♯)
No, no, no, no.

Bridge | F♯/A♯ | F♯/A♯ C♯/G♯ | F♯/A♯ | F♯/A♯ C♯/G♯ |

| F♯/A♯ | C♯/G♯ | B/F♯ |

C♯/G♯   F♯/A♯
  No, no, no, no, I will never forget,

C♯/G♯ F♯/A♯
  No, no, I will never regret,

C♯/G♯ F♯/A♯   C♯/G♯   B/F♯
  No, no, I will live my life.

C♯/G♯   F♯/A♯
  No, no, no, no, I will never forget,

C♯/G♯ F♯/A♯
  No, no, I will never regret,

C♯/G♯ F♯/A♯   C♯/G♯   B/F♯ C♯/G♯
  No, no, I will live my life.

Chorus 3

N.C.   **F♯**   **F♯/A♯**
No, I'm not saying I'm sorry,

   D♯m   **C♯**   **B**
One day maybe we'll meet a - gain.

No, no.

       F♯   **F♯/A♯**
No, I'm not saying I'm sorry,

   D♯m   **C♯**   **B**
One day maybe we'll meet a - gain.

       (F♯)
No, no, no, no.

Outro

F♯   **F♯/A♯**
Closer to the edge,

 D♯m   **C♯**   **B**
Closer to   the edge,

       F♯
No, no, no, no.

       F♯/A♯
Closer to the edge,

 D♯m   **C♯**   **B**
Closer to   the edge,

       F♯   **F♯/A♯**
No, no, no, no.

 D♯m   **C♯**   **B**
Closer to   the edge.

Crossfire

Words & Music by
Brandon Flowers

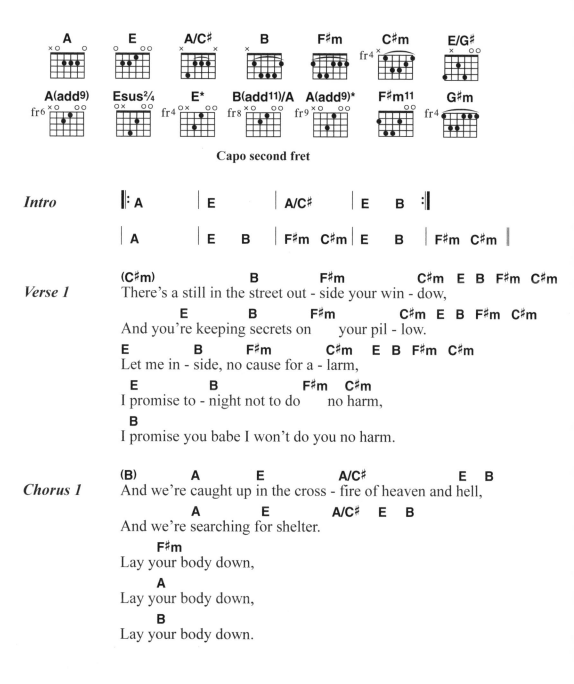

Capo second fret

Intro

```
‖: A        | E        | A/C♯     | E    B  :‖
 | A        | E    B   | F♯m  C♯m | E    B   | F♯m  C♯m ‖
```

Verse 1

(C♯m)   B   F♯m   C♯m E B F♯m C♯m
There's a still in the street out - side your win - dow,

                  E   B   F♯m   C♯m E B F♯m C♯m
And you're keeping secrets on   your pil - low.

E   B   F♯m   C♯m   E B F♯m C♯m
Let me in - side, no cause for a - larm,

      E   B   F♯m   C♯m
I promise to - night not to do   no harm,

      B
I promise you babe I won't do you no harm.

Chorus 1

(B)   A   E   A/C♯   E B
And we're caught up in the cross - fire of heaven and hell,

           A   E   A/C♯   E B
And we're searching for shelter.

      F♯m
Lay your body down,

      A
Lay your body down,

      B
Lay your body down.

Verse 2

```
E                 B            F#m              C#m      E  B  F#m  C#m
Watching your dress as you turn down the light,
        E          B          F#m           C#m      E  B  F#m  C#m
I for - get all a - bout the storm out - side.
E                 B            F#m      C#m      E  B  F#m  C#m
Dark clouds roll their way over town,
E                 B            F#m      C#m
Heartache and pain came pouring down like
B
Hail, sleet and rain, yeah, they're handing it out.
```

Chorus 2

```
(B)          A          E          A/C#                E     B
And we're caught up in the cross - fire of heaven and hell,
              A          E          A/C#   E     B
And we're searching for shelter.
      F#m
Lay your body down,
      A
Lay your body down,
      B
Lay your body down.
      A/C#
Lay your body down,
      E/G#
Lay your body down,
      B
Lay your body down.
```

Bridge

```
(B)          A(add9)
Tell the devil that he can go back
                    E        Esus2/4 E* Esus2/4 E
From where he came,
      C#m                               A(add9) Badd11/A  A(add9)*
His fiery arrows drew their beat in vain.
B(add11)/A  A(add9)
          And when the hardest part is over
              E        Esus2/4 E* Esus2/4 E
We'll be here,
      C#m                                       F#m11   C#m
And our dreams will break the boundaries of our fear,
G#m                A(add9) Badd11/A  A(add9) B(add11)/A
Boundaries of our fear.
```

Chorus 3

      A   **E**
      Oh,___

      C♯m   **B**
      Oh,___

      A   **E**
      Oh,___

          C♯m
      Lay your body down,

        G♯m
      Lay your body down,

       B
      Lay your body down.

      F♯m
      Lay your body down,

       A
      Lay your body down,

      B   **(E)**
      Lay your body down next to mine.

Outro   ‖: E   B | F♯m C♯m | E   B | F♯m C♯m :‖ *Repeat to fade*

Compliments

Words & Music by
Benjamin Bridwell

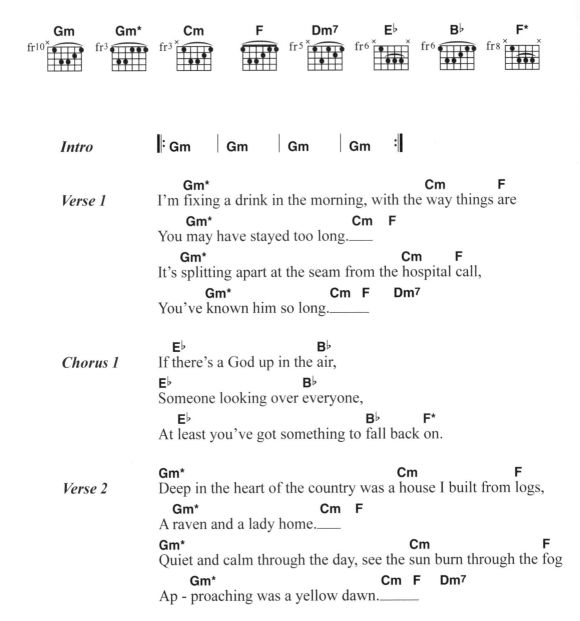

Intro
‖: Gm | Gm | Gm | Gm :‖

Verse 1

           Gm*   Cm   F
I'm fixing a drink in the morning, with the way things are

           Gm*   Cm F
You may have stayed too long.____

           Gm*   Cm   F
It's splitting apart at the seam from the hospital call,

           Gm*   Cm F Dm7
You've known him so long._____

Chorus 1

        E♭   B♭
If there's a God up in the air,

        E♭   B♭
Someone looking over everyone,

         E♭   B♭   F*
At least you've got something to fall back on.

Verse 2

   Gm*   Cm   F
Deep in the heart of the country was a house I built from logs,

    Gm*   Cm F
A raven and a lady home.____

 Gm*   Cm   F
Quiet and calm through the day, see the sun burn through the fog

      Gm*   Cm F Dm7
Ap - proaching was a yellow dawn._____

Chorus 2

E♭   B♭
If there's a God up in the air,
E♭   B♭
Someone looking over everyone,
    E♭   B♭   F*
At least you've got something to fall back on.
     E♭   B♭
And what do people really hope,
     E♭   B♭
Does anybody even care?
    E♭   B♭   F*
I bet you get a lot of compliments down there.

Instrumental ‖: Gm* | Gm* | Cm | F :‖ *Play 4 times*

| Dm7 ‖

Chorus 3

E♭   B♭
If there's a God up in the air,
E♭   B♭
Someone looking over everyone,
    E♭   B♭   F*
At least you've got something to fall back on.
     E♭   B♭
And do you got something to say?
E♭   B♭
Is there something coming over you?
E♭   B♭   F*   Gm*
Do you got important things still left to do?

Cousins

Words by Ezra Koenig
Music by Chris Baio, Rostam Batmanglij,
Ezra Koenig & Christopher Tomson

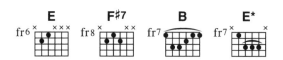

Intro

‖: E F♯7 | E F♯7 | E F♯7 | E F♯7 B :‖

‖: F♯7 | F♯7 | F♯7 | F♯7 :‖

Verse 1

F♯7
You found a sweater on the ocean floor,

They're gonna find it if you didn't close the door.

You and the smart ones sit outside of their sight

In a house on a street they wouldn't park on at night.

Verse 2

F♯7
Dad was a risk taker, his was a shoe maker,

You, greatest hits two thousand six little list maker.

Heard codes in the melodies, you heeded the call,

Oh, you were born with ten fingers and you're gonna use 'em all.

Link 1

‖: F♯7 | F♯7 | F♯7 | F♯7 B :‖

Verse 3

F#7
Interesting colours I discovered myself,

If your art life is gritty, you'll be toasting my health.

If an interest in culture should be lining the walls,

When your birthright is interest, you could just accrue it all.

Chorus 1

E*
Me and my cousins and you and your cousins,
F#7   **B**
 It's a line that's always running.
E*
Me and my cousins and you and your cousins,
F#7   **B**
 I can feel it coming.

Link 2 ‖: E F#7 | E F#7 | E F#7 | E F#7 B :‖

Bridge 1

F#7
You can turn your back on the bitter world.

You can turn your back on the bitter world.

You can turn your back on the bitter world.

You can turn your back on the bitter world.

Chorus 2 As Chorus 1

Chorus 3 As Chorus 1

Outro ‖: F#7 | F#7 | F#7 | F#7 B :‖

     ‖: B F#7 | B F#7 | B F#7 | B F#7 :‖ B ‖

The xx

Crystalised

Words by Oliver Sim & Romy Madley Croft
Music by Romy Madley Croft, Oliver Sim,
Baria Qureshi & Jamie Smith

Bm **A6** **Em** **G** **E5** fr7 **B5** fr7 **A5** fr5

(Implied harmony)

Intro

‖: (Bm) | (A6) | (Em) | (G) :‖

‖: E5 | E5 | B5 | A5 :‖

Verse 1

(A5)   E5   B5   A5
You've ap - plied the pressure to have me crystal - ised,

          E5   B5   A5
And you've got the faith that I could bring para - dise.

            E5   B5   A5
I'll for - give and forget before I'm para - lysed

       E5   B5   A5
Do I have to keep up the pace to keep you satis - fied? Hi-ee-i-ee-i.

Verse 2

E5
Things have gotten closer to the sun,

      B5   A5
And I've done things in small doses.

      B5
So don't think that I'm pushing you away,

          B5   A5
When you're the one that I've kept closest.

Link 1

(A5)   E5
Hi - ee - i -ee - i.

           B5 A5
Hi - ee - i -ee - i.

          E5
Hi - ee - i -ee - i.

           B5 A5
Hi - ee - i -ee - i.

Verse 3

    (A5)   **(E5)**
You don't move slow
       (B5)   **(A5)**
And taking steps in my di - rection.
        E5
The sound re - sounds echo,
   B5   **A5**
Does it lessen your af - fection? No.
  E5   **B5**   **A5**
You say I'm foolish for pushing this aside,
E5   **B5**   **A5**
Burn down our home, I won't leave a - live.

Hi-ee-i-ee-i.

Verse 4

E5
Glaciers have melted to the sea,
   B5   **A5**
I wish the tide would take me over.
B5
I've been down on my knees,
   B5   **A5**
And you just keep on getting closer.

Link 2

 (A5)   **E5**
Hi - ee - i -ee -i.
       B5 **A5**
Hi - ee - i -ee -i.
       E5
Hi - ee - i -ee -i.
       B5 **A5**
Hi - ee - i -ee -i.

N.C.

Verse 5   Glaciers have melted to the sea,

I wish the tide would take me over.

I've been down on my knees,

And you just keep on getting closer.

Verse 5(a)   (Things have gotten closer to the sun,
(Sung with
Verse 5)   And I've done things in small doses.

So don't think that I'm pushing you away,

When you're the one that I've kept closest.)

E5

Outro   Go slow,

B5   **A5**

Go slow, who - a.

E5

Go slow,

B5   **A5**

Go slow, who - a.

(E5)

Go slow.

Dead American Writers

Words & Music by
Gary Lightbody, Peter Buck, Iain Archer, Richard Colburn,
Garret "Jacknife" Lee, Scott McCaughey & Troy Stewart

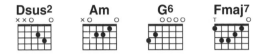

Tune guitar down a semitone

Intro
‖: Dsus² Am │ G⁶ Fmaj⁷ │ Dsus² Am │ G⁶ Fmaj⁷ :‖

Verse 1

Dsus²   Am   G⁶   Fmaj⁷
  Here's to every time that you rock a boat,

Dsus²   Am   G⁶   Fmaj⁷
  Here's to every word that you ever wrote.

Dsus²   Am   G⁶ Fmaj⁷
  There were clues but it was nev - er clear,

Dsus²   Am   G⁶   Fmaj⁷
  You've got to choose your own way out of here.

Chorus 1

(Fmaj⁷)   Dsus²
I could say anything you need, anyone you knew,

                            Fmaj⁷
Anything you see, anything you say,

                           Dsus²
Anything you need, anyone you knew, anything you,

It would be this, it would be this.

Link 1
│ Dsus² Am │ G⁶ Fmaj⁷ │ Dsus² Am │ G⁶ Fmaj⁷ ‖

Verse 2

Dsus²   Am   G⁶   Fmaj⁷
I've been waiting for the spark my - self,

Dsus²   Am   G⁶   Fmaj⁷
I've been scrambling in the dark for health.

Dsus²   Am   G⁶   Fmaj⁷
I have read your words a thousand times,

Dsus²   Am   G⁶   Fmaj⁷
All this spark but smashed up love and crime.

Chorus 2

(Fmaj⁷)   Dsus²
I could say anything you need, anyone you see,

                           Fmaj⁷
Anything you knew, anything you say,

                        Dsus²
Anything you need, anyone you knew, anything you,

It would be this, it would be this.

Link 2   As Link 1

Verse 3

Dsus²   Am   G⁶   Fmaj⁷
I've been chok - ing on the bones and tears.

Dsus²   Am   G⁶   Fmaj⁷
You are the smoking gun that's thrown the years.

Dsus²   Am   G⁶   Fmaj⁷
A broken heart won't get you far e - nough,

Dsus²   Am   G⁶   Fmaj⁷
I'll beat up waiting through the tiring roof.

Chorus 3   As Chorus 2

Outro   ‖: Dsus² Am | G⁶ Fmaj⁷ | Dsus² Am | G⁶ Fmaj⁷ :‖

Death By Diamonds And Pearls

Words & Music by
Russell Marsden, Emma Richardson & Matthew Hayward

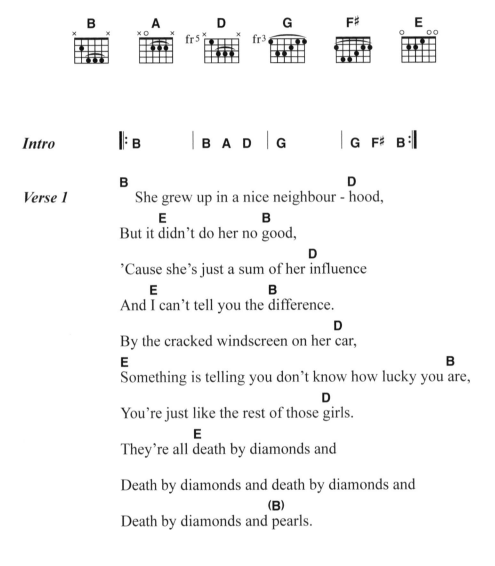

Intro ‖: B | B A D | G | G F♯ B :‖

Verse 1

B   D
She grew up in a nice neighbour - hood,

    E   B
But it didn't do her no good,

                                              D
'Cause she's just a sum of her influence

    E   B
And I can't tell you the difference.

                                              D
By the cracked windscreen on her car,

E   B
Something is telling you don't know how lucky you are,

                                      D
You're just like the rest of those girls.

            E
They're all death by diamonds and

Death by diamonds and death by diamonds and

                            (B)
Death by diamonds and pearls.

Chorus 1

B A D G   F♯ B

Death by diamonds and pearls.

| B | | B A D | G | | G F♯ B ‖ |

Verse 2

B   D

You got your figure all nice,

      E   B

But the heart stays colder than ice.

                     D

You got twenty five grand on the bubble,

      E   B

And you're the one telling me that you don't think you're in trouble.

             D

I might be a fan of your insolence,

E   B

But that don't make you the innocent,

               D

You're just like the rest of those girls.

      E

They're all death by diamonds and

Death by diamonds and death by diamonds and

          (B)

Death by diamonds and pearls.

Chorus 2

B A D G   F♯ B

Death by diamonds and pearls.

B A D G   F♯ B

Death by diamonds and pearls.

B A D G   F♯ B

Death by diamonds and pearls.

| B | | B A D | G | | G F♯ B ‖ |

Instrumental ‖: B | B A D | G | | G F♯ B :‖ *Play 4 times*

Guitar solo ‖: B | B A D | G | | G F♯ B :‖ *Play 4 times*

Chorus 3

B A D G   F♯ B

Death by diamonds and pearls.

| B | | B A D | G | | G F♯ B ‖ |

Death

Words & Music by
Harry McVeigh, Charles Cave & Jack Brown

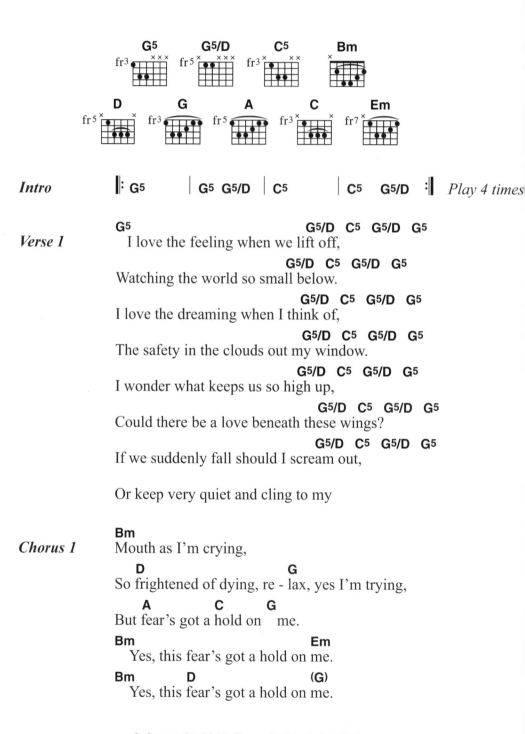

Intro   ‖: G5 | G5 G5/D | C5 | C5 G5/D :‖ *Play 4 times*

Verse 1

       G5   G5/D C5 G5/D G5
      I love the feeling when we lift off,

                                 G5/D C5 G5/D G5
Watching the world so small below.

                              G5/D C5 G5/D G5
I love the dreaming when I think of,

                               G5/D C5 G5/D G5
The safety in the clouds out my window.

                             G5/D C5 G5/D G5
I wonder what keeps us so high up,

                                G5/D C5 G5/D G5
Could there be a love beneath these wings?

                           G5/D C5 G5/D G5
If we suddenly fall should I scream out,

Or keep very quiet and cling to my

Chorus 1

Bm
Mouth as I'm crying,

     D   G
So frightened of dying, re - lax, yes I'm trying,

   A   C   G
But fear's got a hold on   me.

Bm   Em
  Yes, this fear's got a hold on me.

Bm   D   (G)
  Yes, this fear's got a hold on me.

Link 1   ‖: G | G | Em | C :‖

Verse 2
```
G                            Em  C
I love the quiet of the night time,
    G                              Em  C
    When the sun is drowned in a deathly sea.
    G                              Em  C
    I can feel my heart beating as I speed from,
    G                          Em  C
    The sense of time catching up with me.
    G                          Em  C
    The sky set out like a pathway,
    G                            Em  C
    But who decides which route we take?
    G                          Em  C
    As people drift into a dream world,
    G
    I close my eyes as my hands shake,
```

Chorus 2
```
    Bm
And when I see a new day,
        D
Who's driving this anyway?
    G
I picture my own grave,
        A         C       G
'Cause fear's got a hold on me.
Bm                       Em
    Yes, this fear's got a hold on me.
Bm          D              G
    Yes, this fear's got a hold on me.
Bm                       Em
    Yes, this fear's got a hold on me.
Bm          D              G
    Yes, this fear's got a hold on me.
```

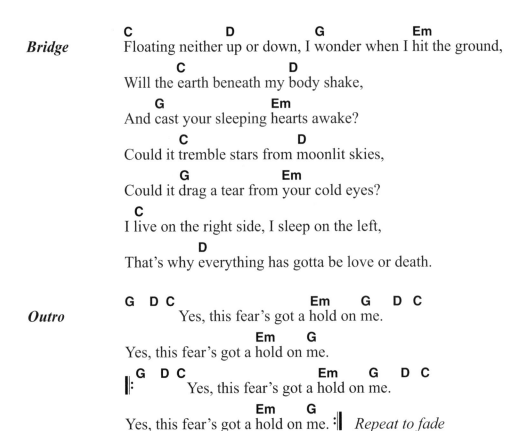

Bridge

```
C            D           G              Em
Floating neither up or down, I wonder when I hit the ground,
         C           D
Will the earth beneath my body shake,
      G              Em
And cast your sleeping hearts awake?
         C              D
Could it tremble stars from moonlit skies,
      G              Em
Could it drag a tear from your cold eyes?
    C
I live on the right side, I sleep on the left,
             D
That's why everything has gotta be love or death.
```

Outro

```
G   D C                     Em      G    D C
    Yes, this fear's got a hold on me.
              Em      G
Yes, this fear's got a hold on me.
  G   D C                     Em      G    D C
    Yes, this fear's got a hold on me.
              Em      G
Yes, this fear's got a hold on me.  Repeat to fade
```

Devil's Spoke

Words & Music by
Laura Marling

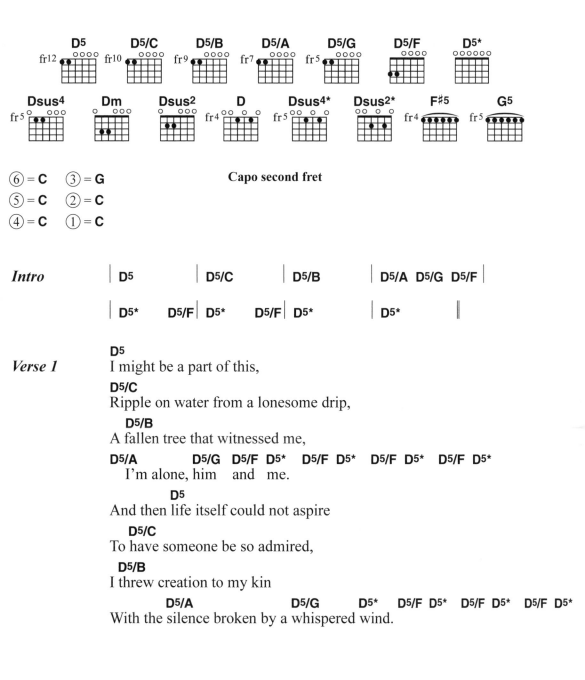

Capo second fret

⑥ = C ③ = G
⑤ = C ② = C
④ = C ① = C

Intro

| D5 | D5/C | D5/B | D5/A D5/G D5/F |

| D5* | D5/F | D5* | D5/F | D5* | D5* |

Verse 1

D5
I might be a part of this,

D5/C
Ripple on water from a lonesome drip,

D5/B
A fallen tree that witnessed me,

D5/A   **D5/G D5/F D5* D5/F D5* D5/F D5* D5/F D5***
I'm alone, him   and   me.

D5
And then life itself could not aspire

D5/C
To have someone be so admired,

D5/B
I threw creation to my kin

D5/A   **D5/G**   **D5* D5/F D5* D5/F D5* D5/F D5***
With the silence broken by a whispered wind.

Chorus 1

Dsus4   Dm Dsus2 D5*
All of this can be   broken,

Dsus4   Dm Dsus2 D5*
All of this can be   broken,

Dsus4   Dm D5*
Hold your devil by   his spoke

      Dsus4   Dm   D5*   **D5/F D5***   **D5/F D5***   **D5/F D5***
And spin him to the ground.

Verse 2

      D5
And root to root and tip to tip,

  D5/C
I look at him my country gyp.

D5/B
Let it up I owe his fears,

    D5/A   **D5/G D5/F D5***   **D5/F D5***   **D5/F D5***   **D5/F**
But someone brought you close to   tears.

  D5
Many trains and many miles

      D5/C
Brought you to me on this sunny isle,

    D5/B
And what of which you wish to speak,

      D5/A   **D5/G D5/F D5***   **D5/F D5***   **D5/F D5***   **D5/F D5***
Have you come here to res - cue me?

Chorus 2

Dsus4   Dm Dsus2 D5*
All of this can be   broken,

Dsus4   Dm Dsus2 D5*
All of this can be   broken,

Dsus4   Dm D5*
Hold your devil by   his spoke

      Dsus4   Dm   D5*   **D5/F D5***   **D5/F D5***   **D5/F D5***
And spin him to the ground.

Link 1   ‖: **D** | **Dsus4*** | **D** | **Dsus2*** :‖

Bridge

Dsus2 Dsus4* D Dsus2* D5* Dsus4* D Dsus2* D5* Dsus4*
But the love   of your   life lives   but lies   no more

D   Dsus2* D5* Dsus4* D Dsus2* D5*   D5/F D5*   D5/F D5*   D5/F D5*
And where she lay   a flower grows.

    Dsus4* D   Dsus2* D5*   Dsus4* D   Dsus2*
And the arms   have fed   and the babes have wed

D5*   Dsus4* D   Dsus2* D5*
And the backs   have bled,

Dsus4* D   Dsus2* D5*   D5/F D5*   D5/F D5*   D5/F D5*
Keep - ing her in   tow.

F#5   G5   D5*
   But I am your keep - er,

F#5   G5   D5*
   And I hold your face away from light.

F#5   G5   D5*
   I am yours till they come,

F#5   G5   D5*
   I am yours till they come.

Verse 3

D5   D5/C
   Eye to eye,   nose to nose,

D5/B   D5/A
   Ripping off each others clothes

                D5/G D5/F D5*   D5/F D5*   D5/F D5*   D5/F D5*
In a most pe - cu - liar   way.

D5   D5/C
   Eye to eye,   nose to nose,

D5/B   D5/A
   Ripping off each others clothes

                D5/G D5/F D5*   D5/F D5*   D5/F D5*   D5/F D5*
In a most pe - cu - liar   way.

Outro

D5   D5/C   D5/B   D5/A   D5/G D5/F D5*
Mmm, mmm, mmm, mmm.

Die By The Drop

Words & Music by
Alison Mosshart, Jack Lawrence & Dean Fertita

Intro ‖: E5 | E5 | E5 | E5 :‖

riff 1

| E5 G E D E

Verse 1

E5
Let's dig a hole in the sand, brother,

                          riff 1
A little grave we can fill together.

E5
   I got myself a problem

                    riff 1
That I been looking to sell.

Pre-chorus 1

E5
Some people die just a little, (some people die just a little,)

                             riff 1
Sometimes you die by the drop. (sometimes you die by the drop.)

E5
   Some people die in the middle, (some people die in the middle,)

                    riff 1
I live just fine on the top.

riff 2

E	G	A	D	E	G	E
7fr	5fr	7fr	7fr	7fr	5fr	7fr
⑤	④	④	③	⑤	④	⑤

Chorus 1

                              riff 1   **riff 2**
I'm gonna take you for worse or better,

        riff 1   **riff 2**
I'm gonna make you for worse or better.

        riff 1   **riff 2**
I'm gonna take you for worse or better

   riff 1   E5
To my little grave.

Link 1

| E5 | | riff 1 | | E5 | | riff 1 | ‖ |

Verse 2

E5
I never said we was equal, (I never said we was equal,)

          riff 1
I never wished to be saved. (I never wished to be saved.)

E5
  If I'm a problem then preacher, (if I'm a problem preacher,)

       riff 1
Let's dig a little grave.

Chorus 2

riff 2   **riff 1**   **riff 2**
  I'm gonna take you for worse or better,

        riff 1   **riff 2**
I'm gonna make you for worse or better.

        riff 1   **riff 2**
I'm gonna take you for worse or better,

   riff 1   E5
To my little grave.

Link 2

| E5 | | riff 1 | | E5 | | riff 1 | ‖ |

Verse 3

E5
Let's dig a hole in the sand, brother,

              riff 1
Slide off the land for worse or better.

E5
  Get right down to the bottom,

          riff 1
If one goes I'll do the other.

Pre-chorus 2 **E5**
Some people die just a little, (some people die just a little,)

                                           riff 1
Sometimes you die by the drop. (sometimes you die by the drop.)

E5
  Some people die in the middle, (some people die in the middle,)

                       riff 1
I live just fine on the top.

Chorus 3 **riff 2**   **riff 1**   **riff 2**
    I'm gonna take you for worse or better,

             riff 1   **riff 2**
I'm gonna make you for worse or better.

             riff 1   **riff 2**
Im gonna take you for worse or better

     riff 1
To my little grave.

riff 2   **riff 1**
    I'm gonna take you for worse or better, (to my little grave.)

riff 2   **riff 1**
    I'm gonna make you for worse or better. (to my little grave.)

riff 2
    I'm gonna take you for worse or better,

riff 1   **riff 2**
Take you for worse or better, worse or better

     riff 1
To my little grave.

Do-Wah-Doo

Words & Music by
Kate Nash

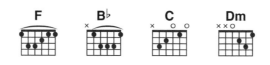

Intro

| F | F | F | F |

| F | F B♭ | F | F C ‖

Verse 1

F   B♭
Everybody thinks that girl's so fine,

F   C
Everybody's like "I'll make her mine!"

F
Everyone thinks she's a bit of all right

B♭   F   C
　But I think that she's not so nice!

F   B♭
Every guy's looking in her eyes,

F   C
Every guy's checking out her thigh.

F   B♭   F
Everyone thinks that girls a la - dy, but I don't,

　B♭   F
I think that girl's shady.

Chorus 1

N.C.   F
I'll just read a book instead,

C   Dm   B♭
I don't care if we're just friends.

F
I can hang out with myself,

C   Dm   B♭
I'm old enough now to   pretend.

F
I'll just read a book instead,

C   Dm   B♭
I know that you think she's best,

F
But I don't even think she cares,

C   Dm B♭
I don't know what you see,

There's nothing there.

Bridge 1

F
‖: Bum-ba-dum-ba-dum-ba-dum-ba-dum.

C
Bum-ba-dum-ba-dum-ba-dum-ba-dum.

Dm
Bum-ba-dum-ba-dum-ba-dum-ba-dum.

B♭
Bum-ba-dum-ba-dum-ba-dum-ba-dum. :‖ _Play 3 times_

F
Bum-ba-dum-ba-dum-ba-dum-ba-dum.

C
Bum-ba-dum-ba-dum-ba-dum-ba-dum.

Dm
Bum-ba-dum-ba-dum-ba-dum-ba-dum.

B♭
Bum-ba-dum. But I think she's a...

Link 1 | F | F | F | F   ‖

Chorus 2

N.C.   F
I'll just read a book instead,
C   Dm   B♭
    I don't care if we're just friends.
              F
I can hang out with myself,
C   Dm   B♭
    I'm old enough now to   pretend.
              F
I'll just read a book instead,
C   Dm   B♭
    I know that you think she's best,
              F
But I don't even think she cares,
C   Dm   B♭
    I don't know what you see,

There's nothing there.

Bridge 2

   F
‖: Bum-ba-dum-ba-dum-ba-dum-ba-dum.
C
    Bum-ba-dum-ba-dum-ba-dum-ba-dum.
Dm
    Bum-ba-dum-ba-dum-ba-dum-ba-dum.
B♭
    Bum-ba-dum-ba-dum-ba-dum-ba-dum. :‖   *Play 3 times*
F
Bum-ba-dum-ba-dum-ba-dum-ba-dum.
C
Bum-ba-dum-ba-dum-ba-dum-ba-dum.
Dm
Bum-ba-dum-ba-dum-ba-dum-ba-dum.
B♭   F
Bum-ba-dum. But I think she's a bitch.

Dominos

Words & Music by
Robbie Furze & Milo Cordell

D5	D	D/F♯	G
x x o x	x x o	o o	o o o

Intro | D5 | D5 | D5 | D5   ‖

D5
Ooh, ooh, ooh.

Chorus 1
(D5)   D   D/F♯
These girls fall like dominos, dominos.
      G   D   D/F♯
These girls fall like dominos, dominos.
      G   D   D/F♯ G
These girls fall like dominos, dominos.

Verse 1
D5
As soon as I love her it's been too long,

Talks of future with you caves me in.

Swallow my sugar kiss and eat it alone,

Hearts collide and smash any dreams of love.

Chorus 2
(D5)   D   D/F♯
These girls fall like dominos, dominos.
      G   D   D/F♯
These girls fall like dominos, dominos.
      G   D   D/F♯   G D
These girls fall like dominos, dominos, (dominos).

Verse 2

D5
Three words we shared, said too early on,

Stuck with forever, flow the point of tear.

Swimming with the fear where we slowly drown,

Ending at never arching melody.

Verse 3

D5
As soon I love her it's been too long,

And I really love breaking your heart.

These silver apples will shine on I was wrong,

The hottest love has the coldest end.

Chorus 3

(N.C.)   **D**   **D/F♯**
These girls fall like dominos, dominos.
        G   **D**   **D/F♯**
These girls fall like dominos, dominos.
        G   **D**   **D/F♯**
These girls fall like dominos, dominos.
        G   **D**   **D/F♯**   **G**
These girls fall like dominos, dominos, dominos.

Link

‖: **D5** | **D5** | **D5** | **D5** :‖

Chorus 4

D   **D/F♯**
Dominos, dominos,
        G   **D**   **D/F♯**
These girls fall like dominos, dominos.
        G   **D**   **D/F♯**
These girls fall like dominos.
        G   **D**   **D/F♯**
These girls fall like dominos, dominos.
        G   **D**   **D/F♯**
These girls fall like dominos.
        G   **D**   **D/F♯**   **G**
These girls fall like dominos, dominos, dominos.

Outro

| **D5** | **D5** | **D5** | **D5** ‖

Don't Stop Believin'

Words & Music by
Steve Perry, Neal Schon & Jonathan Cain

Chords: E B C#m A G#m B/A B/E

Intro

| E | B | C#m | A |

| E | B | G#m | A ‖

Verse 1

E   B   C#m   A
Just a small town girl   livin' in a lonely world,

E   B   G#m A
She took the midnight train goin' any - where.

E   B   C#m   A
Just a city boy   born and raised in south Detroit,

E   B   G#m A
He took the midnight train goin' any - where.

Link 1

| E | B | C#m | A |

| E | B | G#m | A ‖

Verse 2

E   B
A singer in a smoky room,

C#m   A
A smell of wine and cheap perfume.

E   B
For a smile they can share the night,

G#m   A
It goes on and on and on and on.

Chorus 1

B/A   A B/A A B/E E   B/E   E
Strang - ers wait - ing,   up and down the boule - vard,

  B/A   A B/A   A   B/E   E B/E E
Their sha - dows search - ing in the night.

B/A   A B/A A B/E E   B/E   E
Street - light peo - ple,   living just to find e - motion,

B/A A B/A   A   B   E   B E A
Hid - ing some - where in the night._____

Link 2 | E | B | C♯m | A   ‖

Verse 3

E   B
　Working hard to get my fill,

C♯m   A
　Everybody wants a thrill.

E   B
　Payin' anything to roll the dice

　　G♯m   A
Just one more time.

E   B
　Some will win,　some will lose,

C♯m   A
　Some were born to sing the blues.

E   B
Oh, the movie never ends,

　　G♯m   A
It goes on and on and on and on.

Chorus 2   As Chorus 1

Guitar solo | E | B | C♯m | A |

| E | B | G♯m | A   ‖

Outro

E   B
Don't stop believin',

C♯m   A
　Hold on to the feelin',

E   B   G♯m   A
Streetlight　people._____

E   B
Don't stop believin',

C♯m   A
Hold on,_____

E   B   G♯m   A
Streetlight　people._____

E   B
Don't stop believin',

C♯m   A
Hold on to that feelin',

E   B   G♯m   A
Streetlight　people._____ *To fade*

69

Doubt

Words & Music by
Richard Boardman, Matthew Cocksedge & James Cook

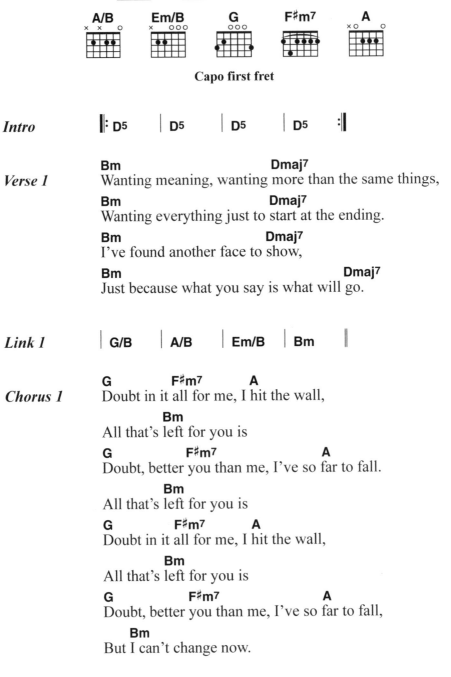

Capo first fret

Intro   ‖: D5 | D5 | D5 | D5 :‖

Verse 1

Bm   Dmaj7
Wanting meaning, wanting more than the same things,
Bm   Dmaj7
Wanting everything just to start at the ending.
Bm   Dmaj7
I've found another face to show,
Bm   Dmaj7
Just because what you say is what will go.

Link 1 | G/B | A/B | Em/B | Bm ‖

Chorus 1

G   F#m7   A
Doubt in it all for me, I hit the wall,
           Bm
All that's left for you is
G   F#m7   A
Doubt, better you than me, I've so far to fall.
           Bm
All that's left for you is
G   F#m7   A
Doubt in it all for me, I hit the wall,
           Bm
All that's left for you is
G   F#m7   A
Doubt, better you than me, I've so far to fall,
           Bm
But I can't change now.

Link 2 | Bm | Bm | Bm | Bm ‖

Verse 2

Bm   **Dmaj⁷**
Missing the life gone by that I had lost,
Bm   **Dmaj⁷**
Missing the better times that I had lost.
Bm   **Dmaj⁷**
When you're near me I get tired when you follow,
Bm   **Dmaj⁷**
When you speak what you say is what will go,
       G/B   A/B
Will go,
Em/B   **Bm**
   And you say is what will go.

Link 3 | G/B | A/B | Em/B | Bm ‖

Chorus 2   As Chorus 1

Instrumental ‖: D⁵ | D⁵ | D⁵ | D⁵ :‖

         ‖: G | F♯m⁷ | A | Bm :‖ Bm ‖

         ‖: G | F♯m⁷ | A | Bm :‖ *Play 4 times*

Chorus 3   As Chorus 1

Florence + The Machine

Drumming Song

Words & Music by
Florence Welch, James Ford & Crispin Hunt

| Em | C | Asus4 | A/C# | D | Bm |

Intro | Em | Em ‖

Verse 1

Em
There's a drumming noise inside my head

That starts when you're around,

I swear that you could hear it,

It makes such an almighty sound.

There's a drumming noise inside my head

That throws me to the ground,

I swear that you should hear it,

It makes such an almighty sound.

Bridge 1

C
Louder than sirens,
Asus4
Louder than bells,
C
Sweeter than heaven
   Asus4
And hotter than hell.

Verse 2

Em
I ran to a tower where the church bells chime,

I hoped that they would clear my mind.

They left a ringing in my ear,

But that drum's still beating loud and clear.

Bridge 2   As Bridge 1

Bridge 3

C
Louder than sirens, louder than bells,
Asus⁴
Sweeter than heaven and hotter than hell.
C
Louder than sirens, louder than bells,
Asus⁴   Em
Sweeter than heaven and hotter than hell.

Chorus 1

Em   C
As I move my feet   towards your body,
        Asus⁴   C
I can hear this beat,   it fills my head up
          Em   C
And gets louder and loud - er,
                        A/C♯   C
It fills my head up and gets louder and loud - er.

Middle

Em
I run to the river and dive straight in,

I pray that the water will drown out the din.
          C
But as the water fills my mouth
      Asus⁴
It couldn't wash the echoes out.
          C
But as the water fills my mouth
      Asus⁴
It couldn't wash the echoes out.

cont.

        C
I swallow the sound and it swallows me whole
          Asus4
Till there's nothing left inside my soul.
        C
I'm empty as that beating drum,
Asus4   **Em**
But the sound has just be - gun.

Chorus 2   As Chorus 1

Verse 3

     (Em)   **C**
There's a drumming noise inside my head
      D
That starts when you're around,
    Em
I swear that you could hear it,
       Bm
It makes such an almighty sound.
        C
There's a drumming noise inside my head
      D
That starts when you're around,
    Em
I swear that you could hear it,
      Bm
It makes such an almighty sound.

Bridge 4

C
Louder than sirens, louder than bells,
D
Sweeter than heaven and hotter than hell.
Em
Louder than sirens, louder than bells,
Bm   **C** **D** **Em** **Bm**
Sweeter than heaven and hotter than hell._____

Chorus 3

(Bm) C   **D**
As I move my feet   towards your body,
     Em   **Bm**
I can hear this beat,   it fills my head up
      C   **D**
And gets louder and loud - er,
            Bm   **Em**
It fills my head up and gets louder and louder.

Drunk Girls

Words & Music by
James Murphy, Pat Mahoney & Gavin Russom

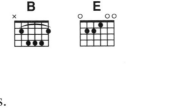

Intro
B
Drunk girls.

Drunk girls.

Drunk girls.

Drunk girls.

Verse 1
B
(Drunk girls) Drunk girls cause a couple of heart attacks,

(Drunk girls) Drunk girls are unusually mild.
      E
(Drunk boys) Drunk boys keep in pace with the paedophiles,
      B
(Drunk girls) Drunk girls are boringly wild.

Verse 2
B
(Drunk girls) Drunk girls get invitations from nations,

(Drunk girls) They got the patience of millions of saints.
      E
(Drunk boys) They steal, they steal from the cupboards,
      B
(Drunk girls) Drunk girls like to file complaints.

Link 1   ‖: B | B | B | B   :‖

Verse 3

    B
(Drunk girls) Drunk girls are like a night of simplicity,

(Drunk girls) They need a lover who is smarter than me.

    E
(Drunk boys) Drunk boys, we walk like pedestrians,

    B
(Drunk girls) Drunk girls wait an hour to pee.

Verse 4

    B
(Drunk girls) Drunk girls know that love is an astronaut,

(Drunk girls) It comes back, but it's never the same.

    E
(Drunk boys, drunk boys, drunk boys, drunk boys,)

    B
(Drunk girls) Drunk girls can be just as insane.

Chorus 1

E
Oh, oh, oh, I believe in waking up together,

So, oh, oh, that means making eyes across the room.

Link 2   ‖: **B** | **B** | **B** | **B** :‖

Verse 5

B
(Drunk girls) Just 'cause I'm shallow doesn't mean that I'm heartless,

(Drunk girls) Just 'cause I'm heartless doesn't mean that I'm mean.

    E
(Drunk boys) Sometimes love gives us too many options,

    B
(Drunk girls) Just 'cause you're hungry doesn't mean that you're lean.

Verse 6

B
(Drunk girls) I've heard lies that could curdle your heartstrings,

(Drunk girls) A couple truths, maybe burn out your eyes.

    E
(Drunk boys) Drunk boys leave their irons in the fireplace,

    B
(Drunk girls) 'Cause drunk girls give them too many tries.

B

Bridge   Drunk girls, drunk girls, drunk girls, drunk girls,

Drunk girls, drunk girls, drunk girls, drunk girls,

Drunk girls, drunk girls, drunk girls, drunk girls,

Drunk girls, drunk girls, drunk girls, drunk.

E

Chorus 2   Oh, oh, oh, I believe in waking up together,

Oh, oh, oh, I believe I'm waking up, but no promises.

Oh, oh, oh, I believe in waiting out the weather,

Oh, oh, oh, I believe in making up. (The day becomes the night.)

Oh, oh, oh, I believe in waking up together. (The day becomes the night.)

Oh, oh, oh, I believe in waking up together. (The day becomes the night.)

Oh, oh, oh, I believe in waking up. (The day becomes the night.)

Honestly, honestly, honestly,

Unless it hurts, why do it?

B

Outro   Hey, hey, hey, hey.

Oh.

Giving Up The Gun

Words by Ezra Koenig
Music by Chris Baio, Rostam Batmanglij,
Ezra Koenig & Christopher Tomson

Intro | A | A | A | A   ‖

‖: A | F♯m | E | D   :‖

Chorus 1

A   F♯m
   Your sword's grown old and rusty,

Bm   E   D
Burnt be - neath the rising sun.

A   F♯m
   It's locked up like a trophy,

    E   E/G♯ D/A   D
For - getting all the things it's done.

A   F♯m
   And though it's been a long time,

    Bm   F♯m   D
You're right back where you started from.

A   F♯m
   I see it in your eyes

    E   E/G♯ A   D
That now you're giving up the gun.

Verse 1

```
A                          F♯m
    When I was seventeen I had wrists like steel
E                 D
    And I felt com - plete.
A                          F♯m
And now my body fades      behind a brass charade
E                 D
    And I'm obso - lete.
A                          F♯m
    But if the chance remains      to see those better days,
E                 D
    I'd cut the cannons down.
A                          F♯m
    My ears are blown to bits      from all the rifle hits,
E                 D
    But I still crave that sound.
```

Chorus 2   As Chorus 1

Verse 2

```
A                          F♯m
    I heard you play guitar      down at a seedy bar
E                      D
    Where skinheads used to fight.
A                          F♯m
    Your Tokugawa smile      and your garbage style
E                 D
    Used to save the night.
E                      D
You felt the coming wave,    told me we'd all be brave,
E                      D
    You said you wouldn't flinch.
E                          D
    But in the years that passed    since I saw you last,
(Bm)                   (A)
You haven't moved an inch.
```

80

Chorus 3   As Chorus 1

Link   𝄆 A | F♯m | E | D   𝄇 *Play 4 times*

Bridge
     A   F♯m
𝄆 I see you shine in your way,

     E   D
Go on, go on, go on.

A   F♯m
 I see you shine in your way,

     E   D
Go on, go on, go on. 𝄇 *Play 3 times*

A   F♯m
 (I see you shine in your way,

     E   D
Go on, go on, go on.

A   F♯m
 I see you shine in your way,

     E   D
Go on, go on, go on.)

Chorus 4   As Chorus 1

Echoes

Words & Music by
Jamie Reynolds, James Righton & Simon Taylor-Davis

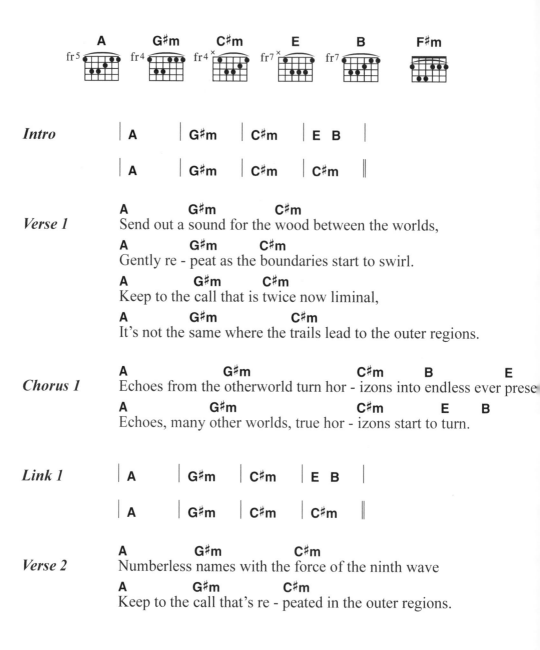

Intro
| A | G♯m | C♯m | E B |
| A | G♯m | C♯m | C♯m ‖

Verse 1
A   G♯m   C♯m
Send out a sound for the wood between the worlds,
A   G♯m   C♯m
Gently re - peat as the boundaries start to swirl.
A   G♯m   C♯m
Keep to the call that is twice now liminal,
A   G♯m   C♯m
It's not the same where the trails lead to the outer regions.

Chorus 1
A   G♯m   C♯m   B   E
Echoes from the otherworld turn hor - izons into endless ever prese
A   G♯m   C♯m   E B
Echoes, many other worlds, true hor - izons start to turn.

Link 1
| A | G♯m | C♯m | E B |
| A | G♯m | C♯m | C♯m ‖

Verse 2
A   G♯m   C♯m
Numberless names with the force of the ninth wave
A   G♯m   C♯m
Keep to the call that's re - peated in the outer regions.

Chorus 2

```
A            G♯m              C♯m      B        E
```
Echoes from the otherworld turn hor - izons into endless ever present,
```
A            G♯m              C♯m      E   B
```
Echoes, many other worlds, true hor - izon takes a turn.

Bridge

```
A               G♯m        C♯m  B   E
```
Echoes reflect and change, they sere - nade.
```
A               G♯m        C♯m  E   B
```
Echoes reflect and change, they sere - nade.

Link 2

```
| A      | G♯m   | C♯m   | E         |

| A      | G♯m   | C♯m   | E  B     ‖
```

Chorus 3

```
A            G♯m              C♯m      E        B
```
Echoes from the otherworld turn hor - izons into endless ever present,
```
A        G♯m              C♯m          B        E
```
Echoes, many other worlds, true hor - izon makes the endless ever present.
```
F♯m      G♯m              C♯m      B        E
```
Echoes into other worlds true hor - izons into endless ever present,
```
F♯m          G♯m              C♯m      E  B
```
Echoes, many other worlds, true hor - izons start to turn.

Outro

```
A            G♯m        C♯m  E   B
```
Echoes reflect and change, they sere - nade.
```
A            G♯m        C♯m  B   E
```
Echoes reflect and change, they sere - nade.
```
F♯m G♯m      C♯m  B   E
```
They sere - nade,
```
F♯m G♯m  C♯m
```
Serenade.

The High Road

Words & Music by
James Mercer & Brian Burton

Intro ‖: Dm | C | G | G :‖ *Play 4 times*

Verse 1

    Dm   C   Dm
We're bound to wait all night,

        C   Dm
She's bound to run amok.

      C   G
In - vested enough in it anyhow,

            Dm
To each his own.

      C   Dm
The garden needs sorting out,

      C   Dm
She curls her lips on the bow,

      C   G
And I don't know if I'm dead or not to anyone.

Chorus 1

Dm   C   Dm
Come on and get the mini - mum,

      C   Dm
Be - fore you open up your eyes.

      C   G
This army has so many heads to analyse

Dm   C   Dm
Come on and get your over - dose,

    C   Dm
Col - lect it at the border - line,

      C
And they want to get up in your head.

Bridge 1

     (G)   **Dm**   **C**   **G**
'Cause they know, and so do I,

        Dm   **C**   **G**
The high road is hard to find.

        Dm   **C**   **G**
A detour to your new life,

        Dm   **C**   **G**
Tell all of your friends good - bye.

Verse 2

   Dm   **C**   **Dm**
The dawn to end all nights,

       C   **Dm**
That's all we hoped it was.

     C   **G**
A break form the warfare in your house,

           Dm
To each his own.

     C   **Dm**
The soldier is bailing out,

     C   **Dm**
He curled his lips on a bow,

      C   **G**
And I don't know if the dead can talk to anyone.

Chorus 2

   Dm   **C**   **Dm**
Come on and get the mini - mum,

    C   **Dm**
Be - fore you open up your eyes.

    C   **G**   **Dm**
This army has so many hands, are you one of us?

    C   **Dm**
Come on and get your over - dose,

    C   **Dm**
Col - lect it at the border - line,

      C   **G**
And they want to get up in your head.

Bridge 2   As Bridge 1

Link | F   G | Dm | F   G | Am G ‖

Outro

C   F
It's too late to change your mind,

      Dm   G
You let loss be your guide.

C   F
It's too late to change your mind,

      Dm   G
You let loss be your guide.

C   F
It's too late to change your mind,

      Dm   G
You let loss be your guide.

C   F
It's too late to change your mind,

      Dm   G
You let loss be your guide.

Metric

Eclipse (All Yours)

Words by Emily Haines & James Shaw
Music by Emily Haines, James Shaw & Howard Shore

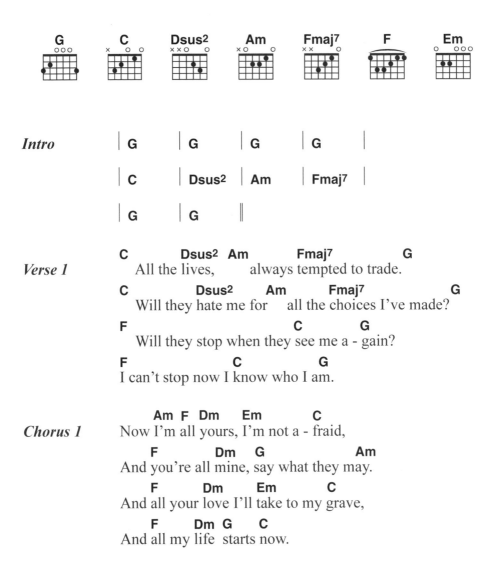

Intro

| G | G | G | G |

| C | Dsus2 | Am | Fmaj7 |

| G | G |

Verse 1

C   Dsus2 Am   Fmaj7   G
All the lives,   always tempted to trade.

C   Dsus2   Am   Fmaj7   G
Will they hate me for   all the choices I've made?

F   C   G
Will they stop when they see me a - gain?

F   C   G
I can't stop now I know who I am.

Chorus 1

Am F Dm   Em   C
Now I'm all yours, I'm not a - fraid,

F   Dm G   Am
And you're all mine, say what they may.

F   Dm   Em   C
And all your love I'll take to my grave,

F   Dm G   C
And all my life starts now.

Verse 2

   C   Dsus2   Am   Fmaj7   G
Tear me down they can't take you out of my thoughts,

   C   Dsus2   Am   Fmaj7   G
Under every scar   there's a battle I've lost.

   F   C   G
Will they stop when they see us a - gain?

   F   C   G
I can't stop now I know who I am.

Chorus 2

    Am F Dm   Em   C
Now I'm all yours, I'm not a - fraid,

      F   Dm G   Am
And you're all mine, say what they may.

      F   Dm   Em   C
And all your love I'll take to my grave,

      F   Dm G
And all my life starts.

Chorus 3

   Am F Dm   Em   C
I'm all yours, I'm not a - fraid,

     F   Dm G   Am
And you're all mine, say what they may.

     F   Dm   Em   C
And all your love I'll take to my grave,

     F   Dm G   C
And all my life starts, starts now.

Empire State Of Mind

Words & Music by
Shawn Carter, Alexander Shuckburgh, Janet Sewell-Ulepic,
Alicia Keys, Angela Hunte, Sylvia Robinson & Bert Keyes

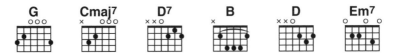

G   Cmaj7   D7   B   D   Em7

Tune guitar down a semitone to match recording

Intro | G | G | G | G ||

Verse 1 (Rap)

N.C.
Yeah,

Cmaj7   **G**
    Yeah, I'm up at Brooklyn, now I'm down in Tribeca,

Right next to De Niro, but I'll be hood forever.

        D7   **Cmaj7**
I'm the new Si - natra, and since I made it here,

I can make it anywhere, yeah they love me everywhere.

            G
I used to cop in Harlem,

All of my Dominicanos right there up on Broadway

Brought me back to that McDonalds,

        D7   **Cmaj7**
Took it to my stash spot, 560 State Street,

Catch me in the kitchen like a Simmons whipping pastry,

           G
Cruising down 8th Street, off-white Lexus,

Driving so slow but BK is from Texas,

        D7   **Cmaj7**
Me, I'm up at Bed-Stuy, home of that boy Biggie,

Now I live on Billboard and I brought my boys with me.

                    G
Say what up to Ty Ty, still sipping Mai Tais,

Sitting courtside Knicks and Nets give me high fives.
Cmaj7   **B**
Nigga I be spiked out, I can trip a referee,

Tell by my attitude that I most definitely from…

Chorus 1
Cmaj7   **G**
New York, concrete jungle where dreams are made of,
               D   **Cmaj7**
There's nothing you can't do now you're in New York.
                    G
These streets will make you feel brand new,
          D
Big lights will in - spire you,
               Cmaj7
Let's hear it for New York, New York, New York.

Verse 2 (Rap)
Cmaj7   **G**
Catch me at the X with O.G. at a Yankee game,

Shit, I made the Yankee hat more famous than a Yankee can,
       D7   **Cmaj7**
You should know I bleed Blue, but I ain't a crip though,

But I got a gang of niggas walking with my click though.
           G
Welcome to the melting pot, corners where we selling rock,

Afrika Bambaata shit, home of the hip hop,
      D7 **Cmaj7**
Yellow cab, gypsy cab, dollar cab, holla back,

For foreigners it ain't fitting, act like they forgot how to act.

cont.   Eight million stories out there and they're naked,

Cities it's a pity half of y'all won't make it,
          D⁷   Cmaj⁷
Me, I gotta plug Special Ed, "I got it made,"

If Jeezy payin' LeBron, I'm paying Dwayne Wade,
          G
Three dice cee-lo, three card Monte,

Labor Day parade, rest in peace Bob Marley,
Cmaj⁷   B
Statue of Liberty, long live the World Trade,

Long live the king yo, I'm from the Empire State that's...

Chorus 2   As Chorus 1

                Cmaj⁷
Verse 3 (Rap) Lights is blinding, girls need blinders

So they can step out of bounds quick,
          D⁷   Cmaj⁷
The side lines is blind with casualties,

Who sip the life casually, then gradually become worse.

Don't bite the apple Eve,
G
   Caught up in the in-crowd, now you're in style,

And in the winter gets cold 'En vogue' with your skin out,
D⁷   Cmaj⁷
   The city of sin is a pity on a whim,

Good girls gone bad, the city's filled with them.
G
Mommy took a bus trip and now she got her bust out,
                              D⁷   Cmaj⁷
Everybody ride her, just like a bus route.

Hail Mary to the city, you're a virgin,

And Jesus can't save you, life starts when the church ends.

cont.

    G
Came here for school, graduated to the high life,

                  Cmaj7
Ball players, rap stars, addicted to the limelight,

B
MDMA got you feeling like a champion,

The city never sleeps, better slip you a Ambien.

Chorus 3   As Chorus 1

Cmaj7
Bridge   One hand in the air for the big city,

Street lights, big dreams all looking pretty,

D
No place in the world that can compare,

Em7   **B**
Put your lighters in the air, everybody say yeah, yeah.

          Cmaj7   **G**
Chorus 4   In New York, concrete jungle where dreams are made of,

                      D   **Cmaj7**
There's nothing you can't do now you're in New York.

                    G
These streets will make you feel brand new,

             D
Big lights will in - spire you,

           Cmaj7   **G**
Let's hear it for New York, New York, New York.

Fader

Words & Music by
Words & Music by Tobias Dundas & Abby Mandagi

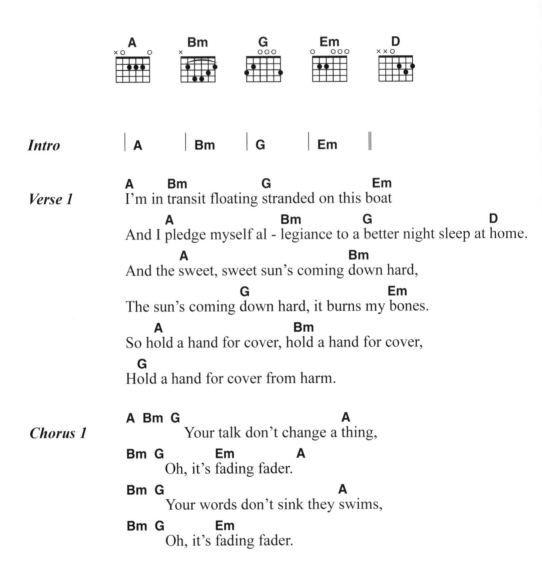

Intro | A | Bm | G | Em   ‖

Verse 1

    A   Bm   G   Em
I'm in transit floating stranded on this boat
            A   Bm   G   D
And I pledge myself al - legiance to a better night sleep at home.
             A   Bm
And the sweet, sweet sun's coming down hard,
                   G   Em
The sun's coming down hard, it burns my bones.
       A   Bm
So hold a hand for cover, hold a hand for cover,
    G
Hold a hand for cover from harm.

Chorus 1

A Bm G   A
       Your talk don't change a thing,
Bm G   Em   A
    Oh, it's fading fader.
Bm G   A
    Your words don't sink they swims,
Bm G   Em
    Oh, it's fading fader.

Verse 2

A   Bm   G   Em
Bless this mess, we tried our best, that's all that we can do.

         A   **Bm**
While the angels walk with the lonely ones

     G   **D**
In the cold rain to rescue you.

       A   **Bm**
And this fable world's coming down hard,

           G   **Em**
The wall's coming down hard on all our homes.

    A   **Bm**
So hold a hand for cover, hold a hand for cover,

  G
Hold a hand for cover from harm.

Chorus 2   As Chorus 1

Guitar solo | **A** | **Bm** | **G** | **G** |

                    | **A** | **Bm** | **G** | **G Em** ‖

Chorus 3   **A Bm G**   **A**
                      Your talk don't change a thing,

Bm G   **Em**   **A**
    Oh, it's fading fader.

Bm G   **A**
      Your words don't sink they swims,

Bm G   **Em**
    Oh, it's fading fader.

A Bm G
      Oh, it's fading fader.

A Bm G
      Oh, it's fading fader.

A Bm G
      Oh, it's fading fader. *To fade*

The Fixer

Words & Music by
Eddie Vedder, Mike McCready,
Stone Gossard & Matthew Cameron

(Chord diagrams: B5, D5, G/D, C/E, E/B, A/C♯, G, Em, D, Bm, C, E♭, A)

Intro

B5 D5 G/D C/E G/D E/B A/C♯ E/B

B5 D5   G/D C/E G/D E/B A/C♯ E/B
Yeah, hey, hey.

B5 D5 G/D C/E G/D E/B A/C♯ E/B B5 D5
Ah,   ah,_____ ah.

Verse 1

G Em   D   Bm   G
When something's dark, let me shed a little light on it.
  Em   D   Bm   G
When something's cold, let me put a little fire on it.
 Em   D   Bm G
If something's old, I wanna put a bit of shine on it.
  Em   D   Bm   G
When something's gone, I wanna fight to get it back again.

Chorus 1

Em D   (Bm)   G
 Yeah, yeah, yeah, yeah, fight to get it back again.
Em D   (Bm)
 Yeah, yeah, yeah, yeah, yeah.

Verse 2

G Em   D   Bm   G
When something's broke, I wanna put a bit of fixin' on it.
  Em   D   Bm   G
When something's bored, I wanna put a little ex - citing on it.
 Em   D   Bm   G
If something's low, I wanna put a little high on it.
  Em   D   Bm   G
When something's lost, I wanna fight to get it back again.

Chorus 2   As Chorus 1

Verse 3
G   Em   D   Bm   G
When signals cross, I wanna put a little straight on it.
Em   D   Bm   G
If there's no love, I wanna try to love again.

Bridge
C   E♭   Bm
I'll say your prayers, I'll take your side,
A   C
I'll find us a way to make light.____
E♭   Bm
I'll dig your grave, we'll dance and sing,
A
What's saved could be one last lifetime.

Link
B5 D5 G/D C/E G/D E/B A/C♯ E/B

B5 D5   G/D C/E G/D E/B A/C♯ E/B
Yeah, hey, hey.
B5 D5   G/D C/E G/D E/B A/C♯ E/B B5 D5   G
Ah,   ah,_____   ah.

Chorus 3
Em   D   (Bm)   G
Yeah, yeah, yeah, yeah, fight to get it back again.
Em   (Bm)
Yeah, yeah, yeah, yeah, yeah.
G   Em D   (Bm)
Fight to get it back again,   yeah, yeah, yeah.
G   Em D   (Bm)
Fight to get it back again, hey, hey yeah.____
G Em D   (Bm)   G Em D (Bm)
Yeah, yeah, yeah, yeah, yeah.   *To fade*

Fool's Day

Words & Music by
Damon Albarn, Graham Coxon,
Alex James & David Rowntree

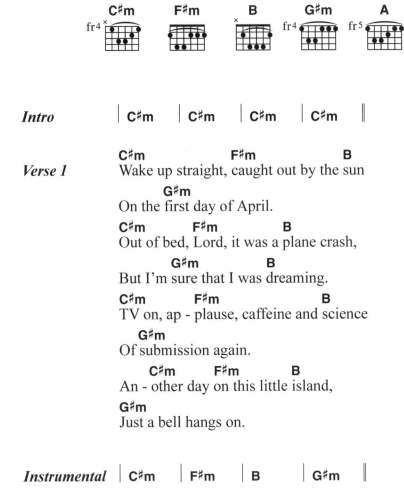

Intro | C♯m | C♯m | C♯m | C♯m   ‖

Verse 1

C♯m   F♯m   B
Wake up straight, caught out by the sun

       G♯m
On the first day of April.

C♯m   F♯m   B
Out of bed, Lord, it was a plane crash,

      G♯m   B
But I'm sure that I was dreaming.

C♯m   F♯m   B
TV on, ap - plause, caffeine and science

     G♯m
Of submission again.

      C♯m   F♯m   B
An - other day on this little island,

G♯m
Just a bell hangs on.

Instrumental | C♯m | F♯m | B | G♯m   ‖

Verse 2

C#m   F#m   B
Porridge done, I take my kid to school,

  G#m
Past the pound shop, Woolworth's.

C#m   F#m   B
Under bridge, where the subway sees the daytime

  G#m B
And the Westway flies by.

  C#m   F#m   B
Then on my bike down the Ladbroke Grove

   G#m
To the forthcoming dramas.

  C#m   F#m   B
The studio and a love of all sweet music,

  G#m
We just can't let go.

A
Let go, let go, let go. let go.

Verse 3

  C#m   F#m   B
So meditate on what we've all be - come

   G#m
On a cold day in springtime.

C#m   F#m   B
Civil war is what we all were born into,

   G#m B
Raise your left hand, right, sing.

  C#m   F#m   B
Don't capitulate to the forces of the market place,

   G#m
They're long departed.

C#m   F#m   B
Consolidate the love we bear to - gether

  G#m   A
On a cold day in springtime.

Outro   ‖: C#m | F#m | B | G#m :‖ *To fade*

The Ghost Inside

Words & Music by
James Mercer & Brian Burton

Em   D   A   Am

Intro   ‖: Em | D A | Em | D A   :‖

Verse 1
    Em   D   A
She sold her love to a modern man,
    Em   D   A
'Cause solid currency's the hardest to lend.
    Em   D   A
All of that money helps you cover your eyes,
    Em   D   A
Don't let the lady finger blow in your head,

Give it up,

Chorus 1
    Em   D   A
For that daugh - ter,
    Em   D   A
She's a star to - night.
    Em   D   A
Without warn - ing
          Em   D A
She gave up the ghost in - side.____

Verse 2
    Em   D   A
Just like a whisky bottle drained on the floor,
    Em   D   A
She got no future, just a life to en - dure.
    Em   D   A
This good Samaritan shaking her hide,
    Em   D   A
'Too Late To Leave Him' are the songs in her car.

Give it up,

| *Chorus 2* | As Chorus 1 |

| *Link* | `| Em      | D   A | Em      | D   A |` |

Verse 3

```
Em                          D              A
   They call it chivalry, never pull a punch for free.
Em                          D              A
   You ever wonder why they had to move on.
Em                  D              A
   This honour code    that put you on your throne,
Em                          D              A
   A double standard you in - voke when you want.
```

| *Chorus 3* | As Chorus 1 |

Bridge

```
(A)    Em
Was it all for show
       Am          D
Don't turn into all of them.
Em
Turn another page,
Am
Trust me darlin',
      D                      Em
I'm carving 'em up through the dust in your town.
Am          D          Em
Crawling over rubble just to sort it out,
Am                  D
Tend to wonder why?
```

Link   `|: Em      | D   A | Em      | D   A :| Em      ||`

Green Grass

Words & Music by
Andy Burrows & Eliot James

Em   E11   B   D   Cmaj7   D6   Am   Bm7

Intro | Em | Em E11 | Em | Em E11 ||

Verse 1

Em   B   Em
You ran a - way to the sun in Cali - fornia.
         B   Em
I'll stay the same, under grey skies I'll come undone.
D   Cmaj7   D6   Em   D6
   And I know on holiday,   the grass so green.

Verse 2

         Em   B   Em
Yes, you ran a - way to find the bright white lights in Hollywood
E11   Em   B   Em
   Some - times in the rain, I think I'd like to burn, I never will
D   Cmaj7   D6   Cmaj7   D6   Em   D
   And I know on holiday,   the green, green grass of holi - day.

Chorus 1

         Em   B
So look down, look down, everybody loves you, oh.
      Am   Em   Bm7
Yeah, my, my, my, can anybody fly this plane home?
      Em   B
And get down, hurry down, there's people waiting for you, oh.
      Am   Em   Bm7
Yeah, why, why, why won't anybody fly this plane home?

Verse 3
          Em   **B**   **Em**
Yes, you ran a - way to catch the sun in Cali - fornia,
              B   **Em**
I'll stay the same under grey skies I'll come undone.
D   **Cmaj⁷**   **D⁶**   **Cmaj⁷**   **D⁶**   **Em** **D⁶**
  And I know on holiday,   the green, green grass of holi - day.

Chorus 2
         Em   **B**
So look down, look down, everybody loves you, oh.
           Am   **Em**   **Bm⁷**
Yeah, my, my, my, can anybody fly this plane home?
         Em   **B**
And get down, hurry down, there's people waiting for you, oh.
           Am   **Em**   **Bm⁷ Em D⁶**
Yeah, why, why, why won't anybody fly this plane home?_____

Guitar solo | **Em** | **Em** | **B** | **B** |

                    | **Em** | **Em** | **C** | **B** |

                    | **Em** | **D⁶**   ‖

Chorus 3
         Em   **B**
So look down, look down, everybody loves you, oh.
           Am   **Em**   **Bm⁷**
Yeah, my, my, my, can anybody fly this plane home?
         Em   **B**
And get down, hurry down, there's people waiting for you, oh.
           Am   **Em**   **Bm⁷**
Yeah, why, why, why won't anybody fly this plane home?
         Em   **B**
So look down, look down, everybody loves you, oh.
           Am   **Em**   **Bm⁷**
Yeah, my, my, my, can anybody fly this plane home?
         Em   **B**
And get down, hurry down, there's people waiting for you, oh.
           Am   **Em**   **Bm⁷ Em D⁶ Em**
Yeah, why, why, why won't anybody fly this plane home?_____

Ellie Goulding

Guns And Horses

Words & Music by
Ellie Goulding & John Fortis

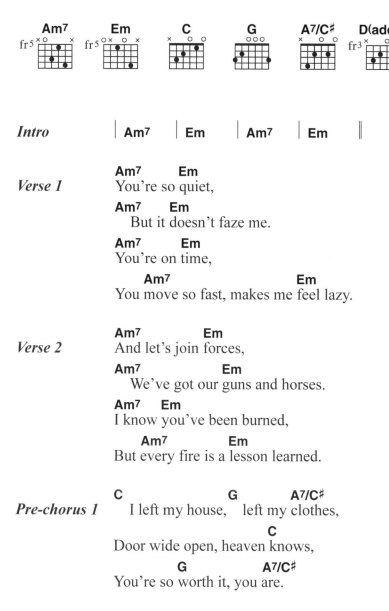

Intro | Am7 | Em | Am7 | Em ‖

Verse 1
Am7   Em
You're so quiet,

Am7   Em
But it doesn't faze me.

Am7   Em
You're on time,

Am7   Em
You move so fast, makes me feel lazy.

Verse 2
Am7   Em
And let's join forces,

Am7   Em
We've got our guns and horses.

Am7   Em
I know you've been burned,

Am7   Em
But every fire is a lesson learned.

Pre-chorus 1
C   G   A7/C#
I left my house,   left my clothes,

C
Door wide open, heaven knows,

G   A7/C#
You're so worth it, you are.

Chorus 1

Em   C   D(add11) Em9
But I wish I could feel it all for   you,

G   C   D(add11) Em9
I wish I could be it all for   you.

G   C   D(add11)
If I could e - rase the pain

                          Em9   G
And maybe you'd feel the same,

             C   D(add11)
I'd do it all for you,

  Em9   Am7   Em
I would, I would, I would, I would, I would.

  Am7   Em
Oh.____

Verse 3

Am7   Em
Let's type words,

Am7   Em
 'Cause they a - mount to nothing.

Am7   Em
Play it down,

   Am7   Em
Pre - tend you can't take what you've found.

   Am7   Em
But you found me

   Am7   Em
On a screen you sit at permanently.

Pre-chorus 2

C   G   A7/C#
  I left my house,   left my clothes,

                         C
Door wide open, heaven knows,

           G   A7/C#   Em
You're so worth it, you are.   Oh.____

Chorus 2

Em   C   D(add11) Em9
But I wish I could feel it all for   you,

G   C   D(add11) Em9
I wish I could be it all for   you.

G   C   D(add11)
If I could e - rase the pain

                          Em9   G
And maybe you'd feel the same,

cont.

C   D(add11)
I'd do it all for you,

Em9
I would, I would, I would, I would.

Bridge

C   D(add11)   Am7
It's time to come clean and make sense of everything,

C   D(add11)   Em9
It's time that we found out who we are.

C   D(add11)   Am7
'Cause when I'm standing here in the dark,

                       C   D(add11) Em9
I see your face in every star._____

Chorus 3

N.C.   C   D(add11) Em9
But I wish I could feel it all for   you,

G   C   D(add11) Em9
I wish I could be it all for   you.

G   C   D(add11)
If I could e - rase the pain

                 Em9   G
And maybe you'd feel the same,

         C   D(add11)
I'd do it all for you,

Em9   (C)
I would, I would, I would, I would, I would.

Outro

| C | | D(add11) | Em9 | | G | | |

‖: C   D(add11)   Em9
    I'd do it all for you, I would.

           G   C
I'd do it all for you, I would. :‖

           D(add11)   Em9 G
I'd do it all for you.

| C | | D(add11) | Em9 | | G | | C | | D(add11) |

| Em9 | | Em9 | | Em9 | | Em9 | | Em9 | ‖

He Doesn't Know Why

Words & Music by
Robin Pecknold

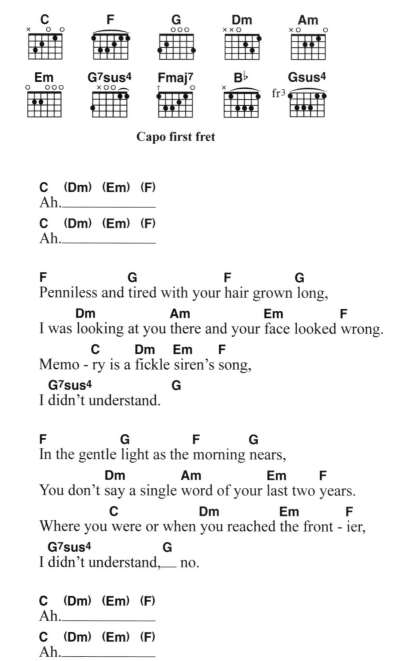

Capo first fret

Intro

C (Dm) (Em) (F)
Ah._____

C (Dm) (Em) (F)
Ah._____

Verse 1

F   G   F   G
Penniless and tired with your hair grown long,

     Dm   Am   Em   F
I was looking at you there and your face looked wrong.

        C   Dm   Em   F
Memo - ry is a fickle siren's song,

  G7sus4   G
I didn't understand.

Verse 2

F   G   F   G
In the gentle light as the morning nears,

      Dm   Am   Em   F
You don't say a single word of your last two years.

        C   Dm   Em   F
Where you were or when you reached the front - ier,

  G7sus4   G
I didn't understand,__ no.

Link 1

C (Dm) (Em) (F)
Ah._____

C (Dm) (Em) (F)
Ah._____

Verse 3

F   G   F   G
See your rugged hands and a silver knife,

      Dm   Am   Em   F
Twenty dollars in your hand that you hold so tight.

      C   Dm Em   F
All the evidence of your vagrant life,

    G⁷sus⁴   G
My brother you were born.___

Verse 4

     F   G   F   G
And you will try to do what you did be - fore,

      Dm   Am   Em   F
Pull the wool over your eyes for a week or more.

       C   Dm Em   F
Let your family take you back to your

    G⁷sus⁴   G
O - riginal mind.___

Bridge

  (G)   C
There's nothing I can do,

      Fmaj⁷   C
There's nothing I can do.

There's nothing I can say,

      Fmaj⁷   C
There's nothing I can say,

I can say.

Link 2

C (Dm) (Em) (F)
Ah._____

C (Dm) (Em) (F)
Ah._____

C (Dm) (Em) (F)
Ah._____

C (Dm) (Em) (F) C
Ah._____

Piano outro

| F | F | C | C | |

| B♭ | B♭ | Gsus⁴ | Gsus⁴ | F ‖

Hurricane J

Words & Music by
Craig Finn, Tad Kubler & Franz Nicolay

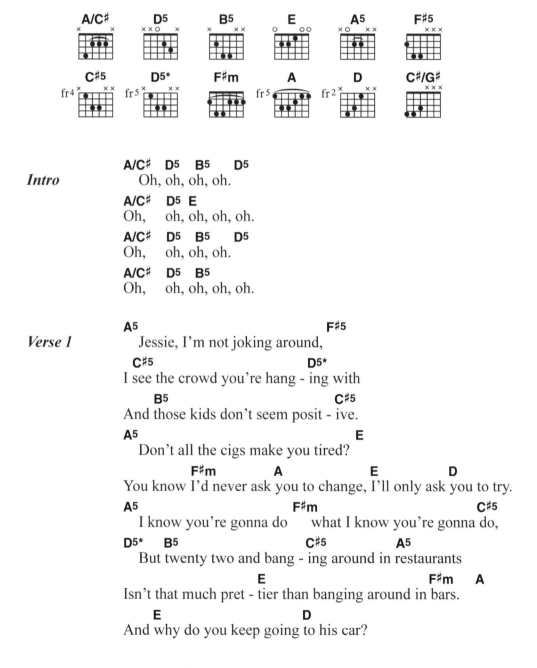

Intro

A/C♯   D5   B5   D5
Oh, oh, oh, oh.

A/C♯   D5   E
Oh,   oh, oh, oh, oh.

A/C♯   D5   B5   D5
Oh,   oh, oh, oh.

A/C♯   D5   B5
Oh,   oh, oh, oh, oh.

Verse 1

A5   F♯5
    Jessie, I'm not joking around,

C♯5   D5*
I see the crowd you're hang - ing with

    B5   C♯5
And those kids don't seem posit - ive.

A5
    Don't all the cigs make you tired?   E

        F♯m   A   E   D
You know I'd never ask you to change, I'll only ask you to try.

A5   F♯m   C♯5
    I know you're gonna do   what I know you're gonna do,

D5*   B5   C♯5   A5
    But twenty two and bang - ing around in restaurants

                   E   F♯m   A
Isn't that much pret - tier than banging around in bars.

    E   D
And why do you keep going to his car?

Chorus 1

A/C♯   **D5**   **B5**   **D5**
I don't want this to stop,   I want you to know,

A/C♯   **D5**   **E**
I don't want you to settle,   I want you to grow.

A/C♯ **D5**   **B5**   **D5**
Forget all the boys that you had at the harbour,

A/C♯   **D5**   **B5**
They're too hard already,   they'll only get harder.

Verse 2

A5   **F♯5**   **C♯** **D5*** **B5** **C♯5**
Jes - sie, let's go for a ride,

             A5
I know a place that we can stop,

            E   **F♯m**   **A**
I know a place that we could drink and kiss for a while,

            E   **D**   **A5**
I know a place that always makes you smile.

                    F♯m   **C♯5**
I know you're gonna say what I know you're gonna say,

              D5*   **B5**   **C♯5**
I know you'll look at the ground,   I know you'll probab - ly cry.

A5   **E**   **F♯m**
You're a beautiful girl   and you're a pretty good waitress,

A
But Jessie, I don't think I'm the guy.

Chorus 2

A/C♯   **D5**   **B5**   **D5**
I don't want this to stop,   I want you to know,

A/C♯   **D5**   **E**
I don't want you to settle,   I want you to grow.

A/C♯ **D5**   **B5**   **D5**
Forget everything that I showed you this summer,

A/C♯   **D5**   **B5**   **(E)**
You're too hard already,   you'll only get harder.

Bridge

E   A5   A/C#   D5   F#5   D5   A5
                But they didn't name her for a saint,

C#/G#   E   A5 A/C# D5
They named her for a storm.

                    A5   F#5   D5   A5
So how's she supposed to think about

        C#/G#   E
How it's gonna feel in the morn - ing?

A5   A/C#   D5
    She said if heaven's hypothetical

F#5   D5   A5   C#/G#
    And if the cigs keep you warm,

E   A5   A/C#   D5
            Then how's she supposed to think about

F#5   D5   A5   C#/G#
            How it's gonna move in the morning?

A/C#   D5   B5   D5   A/C#   D5   E
    About how it's gonna move in the morning.

A/C#   D5   B5   D5   A/C#   D5   B5
    About how it's gonna move in the morning.

Outro

A/C#   D5   B5   D5
Hurricane Jes - sie's gonna crash into the harbour this summer,

A/C#   D5   E
    She don't want to wait till she gets older.

A/C#   D5   B5   D5
Hurricane Jes - sie's gonna crash into the harbour this summer,

A/C#   D5   B5   A5
    She don't want to wait, she said it only gets harder.

Lisztomania

Words & Music by
Thomas Croquet, Frederic Moulin,
Christian Mazzalai & Laurent Mazzalai

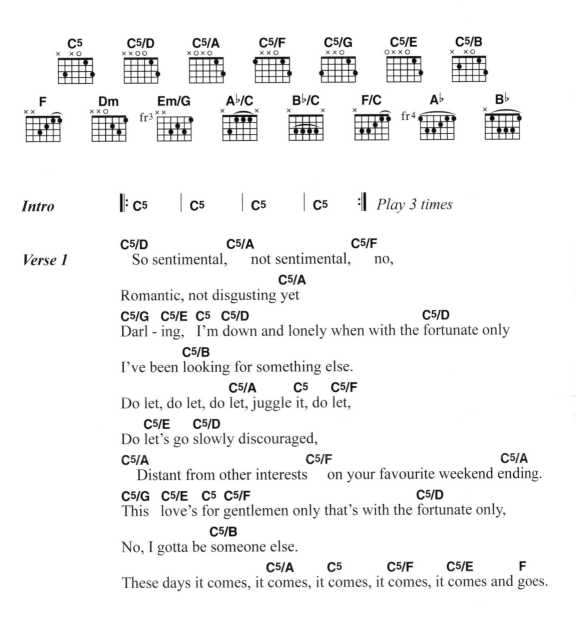

Intro ‖: C5 | C5 | C5 | C5 :‖ *Play 3 times*

Verse 1

C5/D   C5/A   C5/F
   So sentimental,   not sentimental,   no,

                                C5/A
Romantic, not disgusting yet

C5/G C5/E C5 C5/D   C5/D
Darl - ing,   I'm down and lonely when with the fortunate only

          C5/B
I've been looking for something else.

                        C5/A   C5   C5/F
Do let, do let, do let, juggle it, do let,

          C5/E   C5/D
Do let's go slowly discouraged,

C5/A   C5/F   C5/A
   Distant from other interests   on your favourite weekend ending.

C5/G C5/E C5 C5/F   C5/D
This   love's for gentlemen only that's with the fortunate only,

              C5/B
No, I gotta be someone else.

                        C5/A   C5   C5/F   C5/E   F
These days it comes, it comes, it comes, it comes, it comes and goes.

Verse 1

     F   Dm
     Lisztomania,

                         Em/G   F
Think less but see it grow like a riot, like a riot, oh.

                 Dm
Not easily of - fended,

                    Em/G
Not hard to let it go   from a mess to the masses.

F   Dm
  Lisztomania,

                         Em/G   F
Think less but see it grow like a riot, like a riot, oh.

                 Dm
Not easily of - fended,

                    Em/G
Not hard to let it go   from a mess to the masses.

Verse 2

C5/D   C5/A
     Follow, misguide, stand still,

                      C5/F   C5/A
Disgust, discourage   on this precious weekend ending.

C5   C5/F C5/E C5/F   C5/D
This love's for   gentlemen only, wealthiest gentlemen only,

                   C5/B
And now that you're lonely,

               C5/A   C5/G C5/E
Do let, do let, do let, juggle it, do let,

     C5/A   C5/D   C5/A
Do let's go slowly discouraged,   we'll burn the pictures instead.

C5/F   C5/A C5   C5/F
  When it's all over we can barely dis - cuss

C5/E C5/F   C5/D
For   one minute only, not with the fortunate only,

                   C5/B
Thought it could have been something else.

                    C5/A   C5   C5/F   C5/E   F
These days it comes, it comes, it comes, it comes, it comes and goes.

Chorus 2   As Chorus 1

Bridge | C5 | C5 | C5 | C5 |

A♭/C   B♭/C   F/C
  Mmm,   this is show time, this is show time, this is show time.
A♭/C B♭/C   F/C
  Oh,   this is show time, this is show time, this is show time.
A♭   B♭   F
  Time,   time is your love, time is your love, yes time is your love.
A♭   B♭   F
  Time,   time is your love, time is your love, yes time is your love.

Instrumental | C5 | C5 | C5 | C5   ‖

‖: C5/F | C5/F | C5/D | C5/D | C5/A | C5/A   :‖ _Play 3 times_

| C5/F | C5/F | C5/D | C5/D   ‖

C5/A
Outro   From the mess to the masses.
C5/F
  Lisztomania,
C5/D   C5/A   C5/F
  Think less but see it grow   like a riot, like a riot, oh
                    C5/D
Discuss, discuss, dis - cuss,
                         C5/A
Discuss, discuss, discou - raged.

115

I Felt Stupid

Words & Music by
Jonny Pierce

F   Am   G   Em   F/A   Cmaj⁷

Verse 1

    F   Am   G
I felt so stupid, you were standing there
                   Em   F   Am G
You were combing your hair so una - ware.
Em   F   Am
I felt so silly, you couldn't see me,
              G   Em
I know you love your family,
            F   Am
I'm sure you love your family,
         G   Em
But come stay with me, stay with me.

Chorus 1

    F   G   F/A
I don't know if it's right or wrong but come stay with me,
        Am   F
I want to hear every beat of your heart.
    G   F/A
If it's good or bad come be with me,
       Am   F   G
And I'll give you every key to my heart,____
F/A Am F   G F/A   Am
Heart,____ heart,____ heart.____

Link 1

| F | Am | G | Em |

Verse 2

    F   Am
Your arms a - round me
G   Em   F   Am G Em
Seemed to be the only good thing that ever happened to me.
F   Am   G
We can take a walk now down to the beach,
     Em   F   Am G Em
The sun will be shining when we're finally free.

Chorus 2   As Chorus 1

Bridge   𝄆 **F**
          And how've I lived my life too selfishly baby? **Am**
          G   **Em**
          And how've I lived my life too selfishly baby? 𝄇 *Play 4 times*

Chorus 3   As Chorus 1

Chorus 4   **F**   **G**   **F/A**
          I don't know if it's right or wrong but come stay with me,
               Am   **F**
          I want to hear every beat of your heart.
               G   **F/A**
          If it's good or bad come be with me,
               Am   **F**   **G**
          And I'll give you every key to my heart,___
          F/A   **Am**
          Heart,___
          F   **G**
          Heart,___
          F/A   **Am**
          Heart.___
          F   **G**
          Heart,___
          F/A   **Am**
          Heart,___
          F   **G**
          Heart.___
          F/A   **Am**
          Heart.___
          F   **G**
          Heart,___
          F/A   **Am**
          Heart,___
          F   **G**
          Heart.___
          F/A   **Am**   **Cmaj7**
          Heart.___

Outro   𝄆 **N.C.**
          And how've I lived my life too selfishly baby? 𝄇 *Play 8 times*

117

Islands

Words by Oliver Sim & Romy Madley Croft
Music by Romy Madley Croft, Oliver Sim,
Baria Qureshi & Jamie Smith

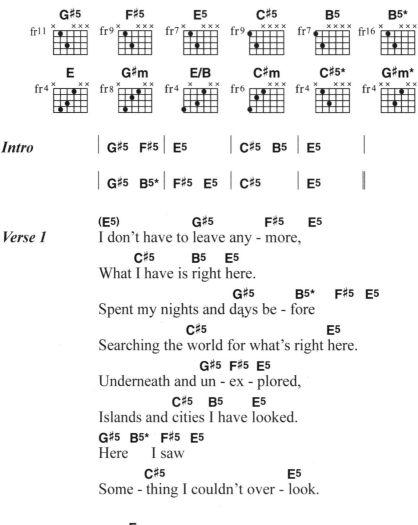

Intro
| G#5 F#5 | E5 | C#5 B5 | E5 | |

| G#5 B5* F#5 E5 | C#5 | E5 | |

Verse 1

(E5)   G#5   F#5 E5
I don't have to leave any - more,

      C#5   B5 E5
What I have is right here.

               G#5   B5* F#5 E5
Spent my nights and days be - fore

        C#5   E5
Searching the world for what's right here.

        G#5 F#5 E5
Underneath and un - ex - plored,

      C#5 B5   E5
Islands and cities I have looked.

G#5 B5* F#5 E5
Here   I saw

       C#5   E5
Some - thing I couldn't over - look.

Chorus 1

      E
I am yours now,

        G#m
So now I don't ever have to leave.

     E/B
I've been found out,

       C#m   E/B
So now I'll never ex - plore.

Verse 2

(N.C.)   G♯5
See what I've done.

F♯5   E5
  That bridge is on fire,

C♯5   B5   E5
  Back to where I've been.

G♯5 B5*   C♯m
    I'm froze by desire,

C♯5   E5
  No need to leave.

                 G♯5
Where would I be?

F♯5 E5
  If this were to go under,

C♯5   B5   E5
  That's a risk I'd take.

G♯ B5*   C♯m
    I'm froze by desire

C♯5   E5
  As if a choice I'd make.

Chorus 2

(N.C.)   E
And I am yours now,

              G♯m
So now I don't ever have to leave.

            E/B
I've been found out,

           C♯m   E/B
So now I'll never ex - plore.

      E
I am yours now, (I am yours now,)

              G♯m
So now I don't ever have to leave. (Ever have to leave.)

            E/B
I've been found out, (I've been found out,)

           C♯m   E/B
So now I'll never ex - plore.

Outro

| E   G♯m | E   G♯m | C♯5* G♯m* |

| C♯5* G♯m* | E   G♯m | E   G♯m |

| C♯5* G♯m* | E | E |

| E | G♯m | G♯m   ‖

E/B   E   E/B
  So now I'll never ex - plore.

It's Working

Words & Music by
Andrew VanWyngarden & Benjamin Goldwasser

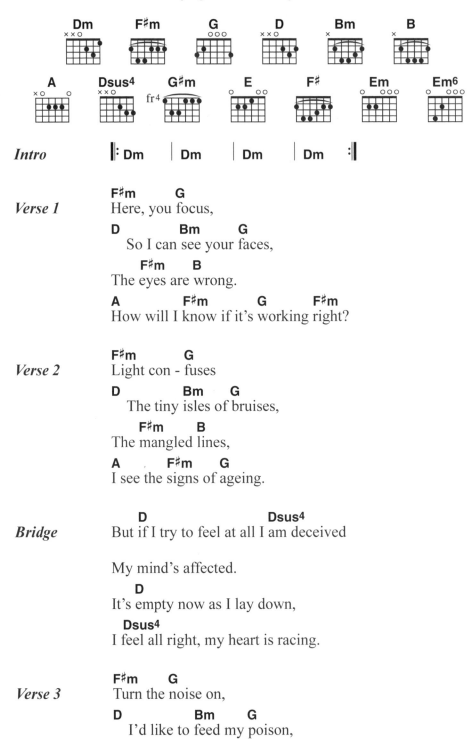

Intro ‖: Dm | Dm | Dm | Dm :‖

Verse 1

F♯m   G
Here, you focus,

D   Bm   G
So I can see your faces,

F♯m   B
The eyes are wrong.

A   F♯m   G   F♯m
How will I know if it's working right?

Verse 2

F♯m   G
Light con - fuses

D   Bm   G
The tiny isles of bruises,

F♯m   B
The mangled lines,

A   F♯m   G
I see the signs of ageing.

Bridge

D   Dsus⁴
But if I try to feel at all I am deceived

My mind's affected.

D
It's empty now as I lay down,

Dsus⁴
I feel all right, my heart is racing.

Verse 3

F♯m   G
Turn the noise on,

D   Bm   G
I'd like to feed my poison,

cont.

   F♯m **B**
As - sembly lines

  A **F♯m** **G**   **F♯m**
Carry a velvet warning.

Verse 4

  F♯m **G**
To the yard.

  D   **Bm** **G**
  It's just like striking matches

   F♯m **B**
The Polish lies.

Chorus 1

  B   **G♯m** **E**
But it's working in your blood,

          Em **F♯**
Which you know is not the same as love,

  G   **D** **Bm** **G**
Love is only in your mind

       A
And not your heart.

F♯m **G**
No, it's working.

Link

| **Em** | **Em** | **Em6** | **Em6** | |

| **D** | **D** | **G** | **Em** | ‖

Chorus 2

 F♯   **B** **G♯m** **E**
  It's working in your blood,

         Em **F♯**
Which you know is not the same as love,

  G   **D** **Bm** **G**
Love is only in your mind,

      A
Not your heart.

Chorus 3

 ‖: **A**   **B** **G♯m** **E**
 It's working in your blood,

         Em **F♯**
Which you know is not the same as love,

  G   **D** **Bm** **G**
Love is only in your mind,

     A
And not your heart. :‖ *Play 3 times to fade*

Ivy & Gold

Words & Music by
Jack Steadman

G   Cmaj⁷   Am   Em   D   Dm   C   G6/9

Capo sixth fret

Intro
| G | Cmaj⁷ | G | Am |
| G | Em | G D | G |

Verse 1

G   Cmaj⁷
Waking sitting upright, can't explain the sunlight
G   Am
Wondering why you're not home.
G   Em
Then I'll go beside you, left before you tried to
G   D   G
Work out all the un - knowns.

Verse 2

G   Cmaj⁷
Blame it all on me when I forget to defend
G   Am
Everything that we worked out.
G   Em
Something in her wording, I cannot help searching
G   D   G
For what memory found.

Chorus 1

Dm   C   (G)
     Thought it stopped just as it start, but that is not what you are.

| G | Em | G D | G |

Dm   C   (G)
     You're a layer on my clothes made of ivy and gold.

Link | G | Cmaj⁷ | G | Am |

| G | Em | G D | G ‖

Verse 3

G   Cmaj⁷
Meet me in the hallway, bite your lip when I say
G   Am
Never have you left my mind.
G   Em
Stop and think it over, smile and move in closer,
G   D   G
Oh what delicate time.

Verse 4

G   Cmaj⁷
Blame it all on me when I forget to defend
G   Am
Everything that we put down.
G   Em
Something in her wording, I guess she was just searching
G   D   G
For some monetary sound.

Chorus 2

Dm   C   (G)
    Thought it stopped just as it start, but that is not what you are.

| G | Em | G D | G |

Dm   C   (G)
    You're a layer on my clothes made of ivy and gold.

| G | Em | G D | G |

Dm   C   (G)
    You're a layer on my clothes made of ivy and gold.

Outro | G | Cmaj⁷ | G | Am |

| G | Em | G D | G | G6/9 ‖

Just Be Good To Green

Words & Music by
Stephen Manderson, Andrew Hughes,
Jimmy Jam & Terry Lewis

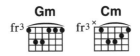

Gm   Cm

N.C.

Chorus 1   Friends tell me I am crazy,

That I'm wasting time with you,

You'll never be mine,

Just be good to me,

Just be good to me.

               Gm   **Cm**

Verse 1 (Rap)   Huh, just be good to Green

         Gm   **Cm**

All I need is a woman to be good to me

          Gm   **Cm**

I'm an easy man, I'm easily pleased

        Gm   **Cm**

And you provide me with every - thing that I need.

Gm   **Cm**

Look, you know I make ends I grind,

        Gm   **Cm**

So hold on to yours, we're spending mine.

Gm   **Cm**

Though you try, I never let you buy,

      Gm   **Cm**

But if I was broke, would you still be spending time?

Gm   **Cm**

    And I believe you would, would,

         Gm   **Cm**

Don't think P's too fucked to treat you good.

      Gm   **Cm**

I'll walk street with you, talk deep with you,

Gm   **Cm**

Even slip and spend all week with you, and I'm off.

cont.

Gm   Cm
 You wish I'd put an end to the torment,

Gm   Cm
Stop, but one thing it's not ever, is boring

Gm   Cm
What would you rather me be like,

   Gm   Cm
I ain't never gonna change, are you ever going to realise?

Chorus 2

Gm   Cm
People always talk about,

Gm   Cm
Look, people are always gonna talk, babes

    Gm
Repu - tation.

    Cm
I ain't even going to lie, shit,

Gm   Cm
 But it ain't like you don't know what mine is.

    Gm   Cm Gm Cm
I don't care what you do to them, just be good to me.

    Cm   Gm   Cm
I'll try, I'll try, I'll try.

Verse 2 (Rap)

Gm   Cm
 Look, babes, you know who I am,

    Gm   Cm
But as crooked as I am, I'll be as good as I can.

    Gm   Cm
I can try and try, though it's evident my

    Gm   Cm
Angel face is disguise for the devil inside.

    Gm   Cm
You're good to me, I ain't good to girls, me,

    Gm   Cm
I'm a bad boy, something every good girl needs.

Gm   Cm
 Honesty can a - void all your tantrums,

    Gm   Cm
But I'm a naughty boy and I always have been.

      Gm   Cm
What, and I ain't changing anytime soon,

    Gm   Cm
I can't have you with me when - ever I move,

    Gm   Cm
What - ever I do, I come back to you,

    Gm   Cm
See, the good attracts me and the crook attracts you.

cont.

    Gm   Cm   Gm
What, we all got our ways, re - member us talking,

    Cm
Of course it was game,

       Gm   Cm   Gm
But it's all gone and changed, now she got me cutting off links,

            Cm
Like I'm trying to shorten my chain.

Chorus 3   As Chorus 2

     Gm   Cm
Chorus 4 Friends are always telling me

  Gm Cm   Gm   Cm
     You're a user,

    Cm
Not me, not ever

  Gm   Cm
Ain't no other man going to treat you better.

      Gm   Cm Gm Cm   Gm
I don't care what you do to them, just be good to me.

     Cm
I'll try,   I'll try, I'll try.

   (Cm) Gm   Cm   Gm   Cm
Bridge I'll be good to you, you'll be good to me,

      Gm   Cm Gm   Cm
We can be to - gether, be to - gether.

      Gm   Cm   Gm   Cm
I'll be good to you, you'll be good to me,

      Gm   Cm Gm   Cm
We can be to - gether, be to - gether.

  Gm   Cm
Outro Why you always listenin' to them,

      Gm   Cm
Why you always gotta listen to your friend?

  Gm   Cm
  Why you always listenin' to them

      Gm   Cm
Why you always gotta listen to your friend?

      Gm   Cm Gm Cm   Gm
I don't care what you do to them, just be good to me,

     Cm   Gm
I'll try,   I'll try,   I'll try.

  Cm   Gm
Just be good to me.

O.N.E.

Words & Music by
Christopher Keating, Anand Wilder & Ira Wolf Tuton

G	C	Em	Bm	Am	D
fr3	fr3	fr7	fr7	fr5	fr5

Intro

| G | C G | C G | G Em |

| G | C Em | Bm | Am ‖

Verse 1

G   C   G
One's not e - nough,

C   G   Em G C Em Bm
I won't stop till I've given you up.____

Am   G   C   G
Here, right as I   am, it's hard having fun,

C   G   Em G C Em Bm Am
It's much easier said than it's done.____

Pre-chorus 1

G
Hold me like before,

C
Hold me like you used to,

Em   D
Con - trol me like you used to.

Chorus 1

    C Am   D   Em
No,   you don't move me any - more

    D   G   C
And I'm glad that you don't,

    Am   D   Em
'Cause I can't have you any - more,

    D   C
But I thought you should know.

    Am   D   Em
You don't move me any - more

    D   C
And I'm glad that you don't,

    Am   D   Em
Because I can't take it any - more.

    D
Oh.

Link 1

| G | | C   G | C   G | G   Em |

| G | | C   Em | Bm | Am ‖

Verse 2

    G
The room's still now when I'm lying

                          Em G C Em Bm Am
'Cause the well of the night has gone dry._____

               G   C   G
When they ask to behave, I pay them no mind,

    C   G   Em G C Em Bm Am
Now I doubt if I'd have been so kind._____

Pre-chorus 2   As Pre-chorus 1

Chorus 2   As Chorus 1

Link 2

| G | | G | | G | | G | |

128

Bridge

```
G              C Em D
Na na na na na
G              C Em D
Hold me like before,
G              C                    Em D
Na na na na na, hold me like you used to.
G              C                    Em D
Hold me like before, hold me like you used to.
G              C
Hold me like before, hold me like you used to,
     Em                    D
Con - trol me like you used to.
G              C
Hold me like before, hold me like you used to,
     Em                    D
Con - trol me like you used to.
```

Chorus 3

```
C  Am        D           Em
No,    you don't move me any - more
D        G           C
   And I'm glad that you don't,
Am          D           Em
   'Cause I can't have you any - more,
D                        C
   But I thought you should know.
Am       D           Em
   You don't move me any - more
D                        C
   And I'm glad that you don't,
   Am       D           Em
   Beause I can't take it any - more,
     D               C
But I thought you should know.
```

Outro

```
     C                    Am
‖: It feels like being tran - quillised,
D        Em                  D G
   I know the separation kills us so.
     C                    Am
But I won't stop falling like raindrops
D        Em                  D
   Because I like it when you lose control. :‖  Repeat to fade
```

129

Kiss Of Life

Words & Music by
Edward Gibson, Edward MacFarlane,
Jack Savidge & Paul Epworth

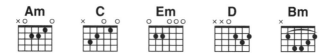

| Am | C | Em | D | Bm |

Tune guitar down a semitone to match recording

Intro

N.C.(Em)
(Kiss of life.)

Rub that line out of the sand, I can feel you closer

Closer than you'll ever be.

Rub that line out of the sand, I know you think it's over,

Staring out into the sea.

Don't let go, this could be so perfect.

Don't let go, if we hold onto it.

Rub that line out of the sand, right before the tide comes

And washes you away from me.

Chorus 1

Am C Em D Am
Ooh,_____ kiss of life.

  C Em D Am
Ooh,_____ kiss of life.

      Bm
Could you wave good - bye to sun,

  C   **D**
The sea, the stars, the waves, the tide?

  Am   **Bm**
The wails inside that life has died,

  C   **D** **Em**
But all you need is a kiss of life.

Verse 2

N.C.(Em)
Rub that line out of the sky, I can feel the night crawl,

On broken drums and tambourine.

Rub that line out of the sky, I can see the clouds form,

Taking shape in front of me.

Don't let go, this could be so easy.

Don't let go, if you hold on to me.

Rub that line out of the sky, right before the sun falls.
(Em)　Am
Kiss of life.

Chorus 2　　As Chorus 1

Link　　‖: C　│ C　│ C　│ C　:‖

Chorus 3

Am　　　　　　　Bm
Could you wave good - bye to sun,
　　C　　　　　D
The sea, the stars, the waves, the tide?
　　Am　　　　Bm
The wails inside that life has died,
　　C　　　　　D
But all you need is a kiss of life.

Bridge 1

‖: Em　D　Am　C　　Em
   Ooh,_____ kiss of life. :‖ *Play 4 times*

Bridge 2

Em　D　　　　　　Am　　C　　　　　　Em
　A thousand butterflies　　from your lips to mine.
　D　　　　　Am　C　　　　Em
A thousand butterflies　　from your lips to mine.
　D　　　　　Am　C　　　　Em
A thousand butterflies　　from your lips to mine.
　D　　　　　　Am　C　　　　Em
A thousand butterflies　　from your lips to mine.

Outro

N.C.(Em)
Kiss of life, kiss of life, kiss of life, kiss of life.

Little Lion Man

Words & Music by
Marcus Mumford

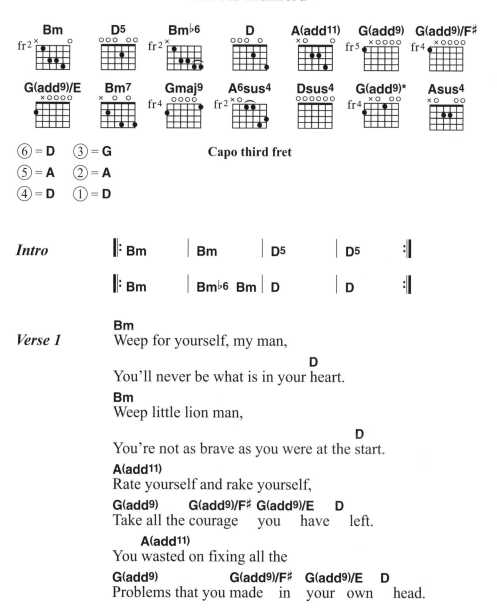

⑥ = D   ③ = G
⑤ = A   ②ed = A
④ = D   ①ed = D

Capo third fret

Intro   ‖: Bm | Bm | D5 | D5 :‖

‖: Bm | Bm♭6 Bm | D | D :‖

Verse 1

Bm
Weep for yourself, my man,

                                          D
You'll never be what is in your heart.

Bm
Weep little lion man,

                                          D
You're not as brave as you were at the start.

A(add11)
Rate yourself and rake yourself,

G(add9)   **G(add9)/F♯** **G(add9)/E**   **D**
Take all the courage   you   have   left.

        A(add11)
You wasted on fixing all the

G(add9)   **G(add9)/F♯** **G(add9)/E** **D**
Problems that you made   in   your   own   head.

Chorus 1

      D   **Bm⁷**   **Gmaj⁹** **D**

But it was not your fault but mine,

          Bm⁷   **Gmaj⁹** **D**

And it was your heart on the line.

      Bm⁷   **Gmaj⁹** **D**

I really fucked it up this time,

          A⁶sus⁴

Didn't I, my dear?

Didn't I, my?

Link 1   ‖: **Bm** | **Bm♭⁶ Bm** | **D** | **D**   :‖

Verse 2

Bm

Tremble for yourself, my man,

  Bm♭⁶   **Bm**   **D**

You know that you have seen this all be - fore.

Bm

Tremble little lion man,

    Bm♭⁶   **Bm**   **D**

You'll never settle any of your scores.

     A(add¹¹)

Your grace is wasted in your face,

     G(add⁹)   **G(add⁹)/F♯ G(add⁹)/E D**

Your boldness stands a - lone   among the wreck.

     A(add¹¹)

Now learn from your mother or else

G(add⁹)   **G(add⁹)/F♯ G(add⁹)/E D**

Spend your days biting   your own   neck.

Chorus 2

      D   **Bm⁷**   **Gmaj⁹** **D**

But it was not your fault but mine,

          Bm⁷   **Gmaj⁹** **D**

And it was your heart on the line.

      Bm⁷   **Gmaj⁹** **D**

I really fucked it up this time,

          A⁶sus⁴

Didn't I, my dear?

Chorus 3

   D   Bm7 Gmaj9 D
But it was not your fault but mine,
      Bm7   Gmaj9 D
And it was your heart on the line.
     Bm7   Gmaj9 D
I really fucked it up this time,
       A6sus4
Didn't I, my dear?
       (Bm)
Didn't I, my dear?

Interlude ‖: Bm | Bm | D | D :‖ Dsus4 | D |

    | G(add9)* | G(add9)* | Asus4 | D5 | G(add9)* | G(add9)* ‖

   Asus4 D5 G(add9)*
Ah._____

     Asus4 D5 G(add9)*
Ah._____

     Asus4 D5 G(add9)*
Ah._____

     Asus4 D5 G(add9)*
Ah._____

     Asus4 D5 G(add9)*
Ah._____

     Asus4 D5 G(add9)*
Ah._____

Chorus 4

   G(add9)* Bm7 Gmaj9 D
But it was not your fault but mine,
      Bm7   Gmaj9 D
And it was your heart on the line.
     Bm7   Gmaj9 D
I really fucked it up this time,
       A6sus4
Didn't I, my dear?
       N.C.
But it was not your fault but mine,

And it was your heart on the line.

I really fucked it up this time,

Didn't I, my dear?
       D5
Didn't I, my dear?

Little Girl

Words & Music by
Brian Burton, Mark Linkous & Julian Casablancas

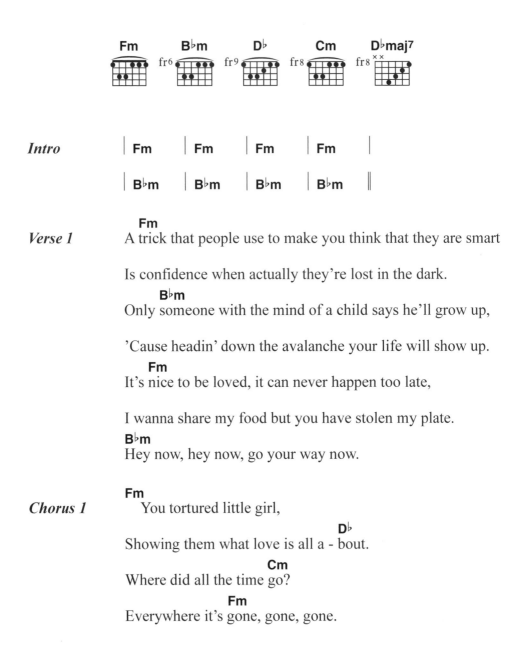

Intro | Fm | Fm | Fm | Fm |

| B♭m | B♭m | B♭m | B♭m ‖

Verse 1

Fm
A trick that people use to make you think that they are smart

Is confidence when actually they're lost in the dark.

B♭m
Only someone with the mind of a child says he'll grow up,

'Cause headin' down the avalanche your life will show up.

Fm
It's nice to be loved, it can never happen too late,

I wanna share my food but you have stolen my plate.

B♭m
Hey now, hey now, go your way now.

Chorus 1

Fm
  You tortured little girl,

D♭
Showing them what love is all a - bout.

Cm
Where did all the time go?

Fm
Everywhere it's gone, gone, gone.

Verse 2

Fm
You get the point now,

You pick yourself up off the bars,

He's on his arm now.

B♭m
'Cause they remind you off the pictures on the wall now

But she was young and I wasn't not even born yet.
Fm
If you think I know a little more then

You have this person on the streets you aren't correct,
B♭m
Because I'm ignorant as shit, not hear to preach, man.

You know I just wanna have fun, go to the beach, man,
D♭maj7
That's all I am, I'm just a simple guy who talks when
Cm   **Fm**
You put a microphone in front of him.

Chorus 2

You twisted little girl,
D♭
Showing them what life is all a - bout.
Cm
Where did all the time go?
Fm
Everywhere it's gone.

Guitar solo

‖: Fm │ Fm │ Fm │ Fm │

│ B♭m │ B♭m │ B♭m │ B♭m :‖   *Play 3 times*

‖: D♭maj7 │ D♭maj7 │ Cm │ Cm :‖   *Play 3 times*

Verse 3

Fm
Running left in a relationship,

Going in circles and I just can't wait.

Running left so we can get in shape,

Get in shape because we can't escape.
B♭m
Running left because I'm running late,

Ending up in the exact same place.

Running laps in your relationship,

Running away from the shadows themselves.
   Fm
The world's always amazed at how much cash you made,
           B♭m
But not at how you made it, it's just strange.

It sounded kind of cool over the 'phone,
                   Fm
It killed your neighbours and they dug and crushed their bones.

Chorus 3

Fm
You tortured little girl,
          D♭
Showing them what laughter's all a - bout.
        Cm
Where did all the wine go?
      Fm
Every night it's gone.

Chorus 4

Fm
You got it all worked out, funny little girl,
          D♭
Showing them what pain is all a - bout.
        Cm
Where did all the time go?
      Fm
Every night it's gone, gone, gone.

Link | Fm | Fm | Fm | Fm |

          | B♭m | B♭m | B♭m | B♭m   ‖

Outro
          Fm
          You're the coolest girl in this whole town,
                                  B♭m
          I just wanna parade you a - round.

          Put your perfect forehead on my face,
                                          Fm
          We can kick this town without a trace.

          | Fm | Fm | Fm | Fm |

          | B♭m | B♭m | B♭m | B♭m |

          | Fm | Fm | Fm | Fm |

          | D♭maj⁷ | D♭maj⁷ | Cm | Cm   ‖

Love The Way You Lie

Words & Music by
Marshall Mathers, Alexander Grant & H. Hafferman

Em   C   G   D/F♯   C(add9)   G/F♯

Capo third fret

Chorus 1

N.C.   Em   C
Just gonna stand there and watch me burn,

                G   D/F♯
But that's all right because I like the way it hurts.

                Em   C
Just gonna stand there and hear me cry,

                G   D/F♯
But that's all right because I love the way you lie.

                Em
I love the way you lie.

Verse 1 (Rap)

N.C.   Em
I can't tell you what it really is,

I can only tell you what it feels like.

C(add9)
   And right now there's a steel knife in my windpipe

G
I can't breathe, but I still fight while I can fight,

G/F♯
As long as the wrong feels right, it's like I'm in flight.

Em
High off of love, drunk from my hate,

                C(add9)
It's like I'm huffing paint and I love it the more I suffer,

I suffocate.

G   G/F♯
   And right before I'm about to drown, she resuscitates me,

She fucking hates me and I love it.

        Em
Wait,   where you going?

cont.

                                        C(add9)
I'm leaving you, no you ain't, come back,

We're running right back.

              G
Here we go   again, it's so insane,

'Cause when it's going good, it's going great,
G/F♯
I'm Superman with the wind at his back, she's Lois Lane.
Em
But when it's bad, it's awful
                  C(add9)
I feel so ashamed, I snap

Who's that dude? I don't even know his name.
G
I laid hands on her, I'll never stoop so low again,
G/F♯
I guess I don't know my own strength.

          N.C.   **Em**   **C**

Chorus 2   Just gonna stand there and watch me burn,
                 G   **G/F♯**
But that's all right because I like the way it hurts.
                Em   **C(add9)**
Just gonna stand there and hear me cry,
                G   **G/F♯**
But that's all right because I love the way you lie.
                        Em C(add9)
I love the way you lie.
                        Em G/F♯
I love the way you lie.

Verse 2 (Rap)

N.C.   **Em**
You ever love some - body so much, you can barely breathe,

           C(add9)
When you're with them, you meet and neither one of you

          G
Even know what hit 'em got that warm fuzzy feeling,

Yeah them, chills, used to get 'em,

       G/F♯
Now you're getting fucking sick of looking at 'em.

         Em
You swore you've never hit 'em, never do nothing to hurt 'em,

         C(add9)
Now you're in each other's face, spewing venom

And these words when you spit 'em.

   G
You push, pull each other's hair

          G/F♯
Scratch, claw, bit 'em, throw 'em down, pin 'em,

So lost in the moments when you're in 'em.

    Em
It's the rage that took over, it controls you both,

     C(add9)
So they say it's best to go your separate ways,

          G
Guess that they don't know ya 'cause to - day

           G/F♯
That was yesterday, yesterday is over, it's a different day,

Sound like broken records playin' over.

    Em
But you promised her next time you'll show restraint,

     C(add9)
You don't get an - other chance.

          G
Life is no Nintendo game, but you lied a - gain,

Now you get to watch her leave out the window,

    G/F♯
Guess that's why they call it window pane.

Chorus 3   As Chorus 2

             N.C.   **Em**
Verse 3 (Rap) Now I know we said things, did things that we didn't mean,

             C(add9)
And we fall back into the same patterns, same routine.

G
But your temper's just as bad as mine is,

                    G/F♯
You're the same as me, when it comes to love you're just as blinded.

                 Em
Baby please come back, it wasn't you, baby it was me,

             C(add9)
Maybe our relationship isn't as crazy as it seems.

              G
Maybe that's what happens when a tornado meets a volcano,

G/F♯
All I know is I love you too much to walk away though.

Em
Come inside, pick up your bags off the sidewalk,

C(add9)
Don't you hear sincerity in my voice when I talk.

G
Told you this is my fault, look me in the eyeball,

G/F♯
Next time I'm pissed I'll aim my fist at the dry wall

Em
Next time, there will be no next time.

              C(add9)
I apolo - gize even though I know it's lies,

                 G
I'm tired of the games, I just want her back, I know I'm a liar

            G/F♯
If she ever tries to fucking leave again,

I'm-a tie her to the bed and set this house on fire.

Chorus 4   As Chorus 2

Many Of Horror (When We Collide)

Words & Music by
Simon Neil

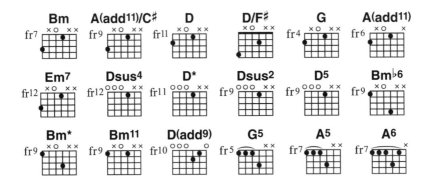

$\textcircled{6} = D\flat$ $\textcircled{3} = G\flat$

$\textcircled{5} = A\flat$ $\textcircled{2} = B\flat$

$\textcircled{4} = D\flat$ $\textcircled{1} = E\flat$

Verse 1

Bm A(add11)/C♯ D
You say "I love you boy."

D/F♯ G A(add11)
But I know you lie.

Em7 D Bm
I trust you all the same,

Em7 D A(add11)
I don't know why.

Verse 2

Bm A(add11)/C♯ D
'Cause when my back is turned

D/F♯ G A(add11)
My bruises shine.

Em7 D Bm
Our broken fairytale,

Em7 D A(add11)
So hard to hide.

Pre-chorus 1

Bm D G
I still believe

D/F♯ Bm G   A(add11)
It's you and me till the end of time.

Chorus 1

Dsus⁴ ... D* ... Dsus² D⁵ ... Dsus² D*
When we col - lide we come   to - geth - er,

Bm♭6 Bm* ... Bm¹¹ Bm ... G
If we don't we'll always be a - part.

Dsus⁴ D* ... Dsus² D⁵ ... Dsus² D(add9)
I'll take a bruise, I know you're worth   it

Bm♭6 Bm* ... Bm¹¹ Bm ... G
When you hit me, hit me hard.

Verse 3

Bm A(add11)/C♯ D
            Sitting in a wishing hole,

D/F♯ G A(add11)
            Hoping it stays dry.

Em⁷ D Bm
            Feet cast in solid stone,

Em⁷ D A(add11)
            I've got Gilligan's eyes.

Pre-chorus 2   As Pre-chorus 1

Chorus 2   As Chorus 1

Bridge

G ... D/F♯ ... A(add11)
   'Cause you said   love

Bm ... G ... D/F♯ ... A(add11)
Was letting us go a - gainst what

Bm A(add11)/C♯ D D*
Our fu - ture   is for.

D/F♯ G A(add11)
Ma - ny of horror,

Em⁷ D ... Bm Em⁷ D ... A(add11)
Our fu - ture's for ma - ny of horror.

Instrumental

G A(add11) Bm D*
Oh.___

D/F♯ G A(add11)
Oh.___

Em7 D Bm
Oh.___

Em7 D A(add11)
Oh.___

Pre-chorus 3

Bm A(add11)/C♯ D G
I still believe

D/F♯ G   **A(add11)**
It's you and me till the end of time.

Chorus 3

Dsus4   **D***   **Dsus2 D5**   **Dsus2 D***
When we col - lide we come   to - geth - er,

Bm♭6 Bm*   **Bm11**   **Bm**   **G**
If we don't we'll always be a - part.

Dsus4   **D***   **Dsus2 D5**   **Dsus2 D(add9)**
I'll take a bruise, I know you're worth   it

Bm♭6   **Bm***   **Bm11**   **Bm**   **G**
When you hit me, hit me hard.___

Strings outro | **G5** | **A5**   **A6** | **D***   ‖

146

MY KZ, UR BF

Words & Music by
Michael Spearman, Jonathan Higgs,
Jeremy Pritchard & Alex Robertshaw

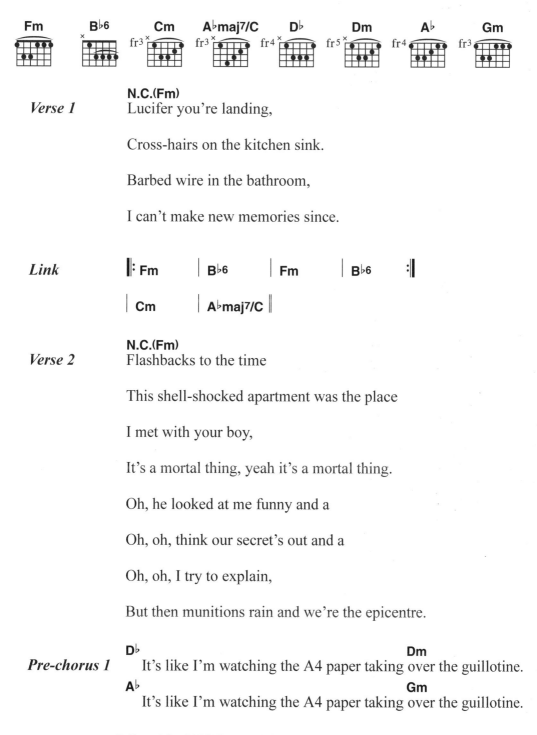

Fm   **B♭6**   **Cm**   **A♭maj7/C**   **D♭**   **Dm**   **A♭**   **Gm**

Verse 1

N.C.(Fm)
Lucifer you're landing,

Cross-hairs on the kitchen sink.

Barbed wire in the bathroom,

I can't make new memories since.

Link

‖: Fm │ B♭6 │ Fm │ B♭6 :‖

│ Cm │ A♭maj7/C ‖

Verse 2

N.C.(Fm)
Flashbacks to the time

This shell-shocked apartment was the place

I met with your boy,

It's a mortal thing, yeah it's a mortal thing.

Oh, he looked at me funny and a

Oh, oh, think our secret's out and a

Oh, oh, I try to explain,

But then munitions rain and we're the epicentre.

Pre-chorus 1

D♭   **Dm**
It's like I'm watching the A4 paper taking over the guillotine.
A♭   **Gm**
It's like I'm watching the A4 paper taking over the guillotine.

Chorus 1

    Fm   **B♭6**
And I wanna know what happened to your boyfriend,

                             Fm
'Cause he was looking at me like whoa.

                                  B♭6
Yeah right before the kitchen was a dustbowl.

                           Fm
And tossing me the keys and I can't forget how

                                    B♭6
That everything was coming through the windows,

                           Fm
And half the street was under my nails.

                               B♭6
It's like we're sitting in a Faraday cage,

                    Cm   **A♭maj7/C**
When the lights all failed.

Verse 2

    N.C.(Fm)
I fly through the walls

All pieces colliding and I

See Raymond apart

He's a-frowning now, wagging a finger at me

Boy, his knees bend the other way and

Boy, boy, are you guys together honey?

B-b-boy, oh, but now I can't find his torso, mm-mm-mm

I guess you're separated, oh.

Pre-chorus 2

    D♭   **Dm**
It's like I'm watching the A4 paper taking over the guillotine.

                  A♭
Monica I just wanna know.

                                            Gm
It's like I'm watching the A4 paper taking over the guillotine.

Chorus 2   As Chorus 1

Bridge

A♭maj7/C Cm   A♭maj7/C
Lights all failed.

Cm   A♭maj7/C
Lucifer you're land - ing

(I do believe it will be business inside)
Cm   A♭maj7/C
Cross-hairs on the kitchen sink

(It's a real spanner into my works I think I kicked the bucket)
Cm   A♭maj7/C
Baby's on the bulls - eye (I do believe it will be business inside)
Cm   A♭maj7/C
I can't make new memories since, -ries since, -ries since.

Chorus 3

Fm   B♭6
   And I wanna know what happened to your boyfriend,
                                    Fm
'Cause he was looking at me like whoa.
                              B♭6
Yeah right before the kitchen was a dustbowl.
                              Fm
And tossing me the keys and I can't forget how
                              B♭6
That everything was coming through the windows,
                              Fm
And half the street was under my nails.
                              B♭6
It's like we're sitting in a Faraday cage,
                              Fm
When the lights all failed.

Chorus 4

Fm   B♭6
And now everybody gotta go hungry,
                              Fm
And everybody cover up their mouths.
                              B♭6
And I haven't seen the body count lately,
                              Fm
But looking at your faces it must have been bad.
                              B♭6
And if everybody answered their 'phone calls.
                              Fm
But people say the army's on fire,
                              B♭6
It's like we sitting with our parachutes on
                    (A♭)
When the airport's gone.

149

Miami

Words & Music by
Yannis Philippakis, James Smith,
Jack Bevan, Edwin Congreave & Walter Gervers

Em   C   Am   E5   G5   A5   C5

Intro

| Em | Em | Em | Em ‖

‖: Em | Em | C | Am :‖

Verse 1

E5 G5 A5 C5 E5   G5 A5 C5 E5 G5 A5 G5 E5 G5 A5 C5
I pro - mised you on an o - cean of

E5   G5 A5 C5
Mo - ther of pearl,

E5   G5 A5 C5 E5 G5 A5 G5 E5 G5 A5 C5
Gold and in - di - go.

E5 G5   A5 C5
Cut through the waves,

 E5   G5   A5 C5   E5 G5 A5 G5 E5 G5 A5 C5
I watched you swim a - way,

E5 G5   A5 C5   E5 G5   A5   C5 E5 G5 A5 G5 E5 G5 A5
I'll nev - er love you   more than to - day.

Chorus 1

Em
Would you be there,

C   Am   Em C Am
Be there, be there for me?

Em
Would you be there,

C   Am   Em C Am
Be there, be there for me?

Verse 2

E5   G5 A5 C5   E5 G5 A5   C5 E5 G5 A5 G5 E5 G5 A5 C5
Now black light sets on   my short day,

E5   G5 A5 C5
Oh, you be - trayed me,

E5   G5 A5   C5   E5 G5 A5 G5 E5 G5 A5 C5
You gave it a - way.

       E5   G5   A5
You don't mind picking up salt

     C5 E5 G5 A5 C5   E5 G5 A5 G5 E5 G5 A5
To rub in - to my wounds.

Chorus 2

Em
Would you be there,

C   Am   Em C Am
Be there, be there for me?

Em
Would you betray me,

C   Am   Em C Am
Or save me, save me a - gain?

Bridge

Em   C   Em   C   Em
Miami bad, Miami bad, Miami bad, Miami bad.

      C   Em   Am C   Em
Miami bad, Miami bad, Miami bad,   Miami bad.

Miami bad, Miami bad, Miami bad, Miami bad.

Miami bad, Miami bad, Miami bad, Miami bad.

Chorus 3

Em
Would you be there,

C   Am   Em C Am
Be there, be there for me?

Em
Would you betray me,

    C   Am   Em C Am
Or save me, save me a - gain?

Em
Would you be there,

C   Am   Em C Am
Be there, be there for me?

Em
Would you betray me,

    C   Am   Em C Am Em
Or save me, save me a - gain?

New Fang

Words & Music by
David Grohl, Joshua Homme and John Paul Jones

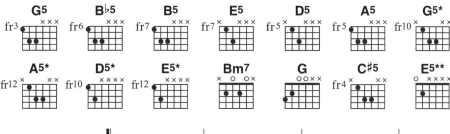

Intro G5 B♭5 ‖: B5   E5 D5 | B5 E5 D5 B5 | B5 E5 A5 G5 | A5 G5   B♭5 :‖

Play 4 times

Verse 1

B5   E5 D5 B5   E5 D5 B5   E5 D5
New fang,   no thang.   Had it made, to parade,

A5   G5   B♭5
Found a sucker, now I want an - other.

B5   E5 D5 B5   E5 D5 B5   E5
Stand up,   step a - side,   open wide,

D5   A5   G5   B♭5
Hanging out and on until the feeling's gone.

B5   E5 D5 B5   E5 D5 B5   E5   D5
Want to?   Yes, I do.   Want to learn,

A5   G5   B♭5
Taking turns getting carpet burns.

B5   E5 D5   B5 E5   D5   B5 E5   D5
Loose lips,   lip - stick spit.   Come and go,

A5   G5   B♭5
I think it's both I gotta know.

Chorus 1

G5*   A5*   D5*   E5*   B5 A5
Sometimes you break a finger on the upper hand.

G5*   A5*   D5*   E5* B5 A5
I think you've got me con - fused for a better man.

G5*   D5*   B5 A5
Sometimes you break the finger on the upper hand.

G5*   A5*   D5*   Bm7
Said you've got me con - fused, ah.

I ain't a better man.

Link 1 ‖: Bm⁷ | Bm⁷ | Bm⁷ | G :‖

Verse 2

B⁵   E⁵ D⁵   B⁵ E⁵ D⁵   B⁵
No slack,   Cadil - lac.   Couldn't quit,

E⁵   D⁵   A⁵ G⁵   B♭⁵
Gums flap so here's your teeth back.

B⁵   E⁵ D⁵ B⁵   E⁵ D⁵ B⁵
  Ac - cept   what I left   far behind

E⁵ D⁵ A⁵   G⁵   B♭⁵
In a time when my mind was like a land - mine.

B⁵   E⁵ D⁵ B⁵   E⁵ D⁵ B⁵   E⁵ D⁵
  Tail - gate, by the lake, too much, too young,

A⁵   G⁵   B♭⁵
Every button gonna come un - done.

B⁵   E⁵ D⁵ B⁵ E⁵ D⁵ B⁵ E⁵ D⁵
  Tight - rope, no joke.

A⁵   G⁵   B♭⁵
Nothing left, so you go ba - roque.

Chorus 2

G⁵*   A⁵* D⁵*   E⁵*   B⁵ A⁵
  Sometimes you break a finger on the upper hand.

G⁵*   A⁵* D⁵*   E⁵* B⁵ A⁵
  I said you've got me con - fused with a better man.

G⁵*   D⁵*   B⁵ A⁵
Sometimes you break a finger on the upper hand.

G⁵*   A⁵* D⁵*   (C♯⁵)
I know you got me confused.____

Instrumental ‖: C♯⁵ | C♯⁵ E⁵ | C♯⁵ | C♯ E** :‖ *Play 4 times*

‖: B⁵   E⁵ D⁵ | B⁵ E⁵ D⁵ B⁵ | B⁵ E⁵ A⁵ G⁵ | A⁵ G⁵ B♭⁵ :‖

Play 4 times

Bridge

B5　E5 D5 B5 E5 D5 B5　　E5 D5 A5 G5 B♭5
New fang　passing　down,　oh.

B5 E5 D5 B5　　E5 D5 B5　E5 D5 A5 G5 B♭5
No more　parad - ing a - round　for.

B5　E5 D5 B5 E5 D5 B5　　E5 D5 A5 G5 B♭5
New fang　passing　down,　ah.

B5 E5 D5 B5　　E5 D5 B5　E5 D5 A5 G5 B♭5
No more　parad - ing a - round,　ah.

B5　E5 D5 B5 E5 D5 B5　　B5 D5 A5 G5 B♭5
New fang,　　new　fang.

B5　E5　D5　　B5 E5 D5 B5 E5 D5 A5 G5 B♭5
　　Ain't gonna wait,　　no._____

B5　E5 D5 B5 E5 D5 B5 E5 D5 A5 G5 B♭5
New fang,　new,　　　ah.

B5　E5　D5　　B5 E5 D5 B5　E5 D5 A5 G5 B♭5
　　Ain't gonna wait,　no more.

Outro　　𝄆 B5　　　| B5　G　| B5　　　| B5　G 𝄇 *Play 4 times*

Notion

Words & Music by
Caleb Followill, Nathan Followill,
Jared Followill & Matthew Followill

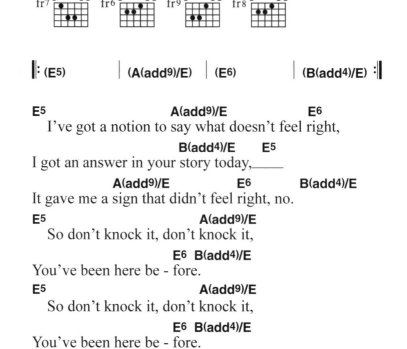

Intro
‖: (E5) │ (A(add9)/E) │ (E6) │ (B(add4)/E) :‖

Verse 1

E5   A(add9)/E   E6
I've got a notion to say what doesn't feel right,

                         B(add4)/E   E5
I got an answer in your story today,_____

             A(add9)/E   E6   B(add4)/E
It gave me a sign that didn't feel right, no.

E5   A(add9)/E
So don't knock it, don't knock it,

                       E6 B(add4)/E
You've been here be - fore.

E5   A(add9)/E
So don't knock it, don't knock it,

                       E6 B(add4)/E
You've been here be - fore.

Link 1
‖: E5 │ A(add9)/E │ E6 │ B(add4)/E :‖

Verse 2

E5   A(add9)/E   E6
I just wanted to know if I could go home,

                      B(add4)/E   E5
I've been a-rambling day after day_____

             A(add9)/E   E6   B(add4)/E
And everyone says I don't know._____

E5   A(add9)/E
So don't knock it, don't knock it,

                       E6 B(add4)/E
You've been here be - fore.

E5   A(add9)/E
So don't knock it, don't knock it,

                       E6 B(add4)/E
You've been here be - fore.

| *Link 2* | ‖: E5 | A(add9)/E | E6 | B(add4)/E :‖ |

Verse 3

E5   A(add9)/E   E6   B(add4)/E
Got a notion to say what doesn't feel right,

E5   A(add9)/E   E6   B(add4)/E
I just wanted to know if I could go home.

E5   A(add9)/E
So don't knock it, don't knock it,

                         E6   B(add4)/E
You've been here be - fore.

E5   A(add9)/E
So don't knock it, don't knock it,

                         E6   B(add4)/E
You've been here be - fore.

| *Link 3* | ‖: E5 | A(add9)/E | E6 | B(add4)/E :‖ |

Outro

E5   A(add9)/E E6   B(add4)/E
So don't knock it, don't knock it.

E5   A(add9)/E E6   B(add4)/E
So don't knock it, don't knock it.

E5   A(add9)/E
So don't knock it, don't knock it,

                         E6   B(add4)/E
You've been here be - fore.

E5   A(add9)/E
So don't knock it, don't knock it,

                         E6   B(add4)/E   E5
You've been here be - fore.

Paris

Words & Music by
Edward Gibson, Edward MacFarlane,
Jack Savidge & Axel Willner

Amaj⁷ G♯m⁷ E C♯m⁷ C♯m⁷/B

Intro | Amaj⁷ | Amaj⁷ | Amaj⁷ | Amaj⁷ |

| G♯m⁷ | G♯m⁷ | G♯m⁷ | G♯m⁷ ‖

Verse 1

Amaj⁷
One day we're gonna live in Paris,
G♯m⁷
I promise, I'm on it.
Amaj⁷
When I'm bringing in the money,
G♯m⁷
I promise, I'm on it.
Amaj⁷
I'm gonna take you out to a club showcase,

We're gonna live it up,
G♯m⁷
I promise,

Just hold on a little more.

Chorus 1

Amaj⁷
And every night we'll watch the stars,
        E   **C♯m⁷ C♯m⁷/B**
They'll be out for us, they'll be out for us.
Amaj⁷
And every night, the city lights,
        E   **C♯m⁷ C♯m⁷/B**
They'll be out for us, they'll be out for us.

Verse 2

      Amaj7
One day we're gonna live in Paris,
   G♯m7
I promise, I'm on it.
     Amaj7
I'll find you that French boy,

You'll find me that French girl,
   G♯m7
I promise, I'm on it.
       Amaj7
So go and pack your bags for the long haul,

We're gonna lose ourselves,
   G♯m7
I promise,

This time next year will be forevermore.

Chorus 2   As Chorus 1

Chorus 3   As Chorus 1

Outro   ‖: Amaj7 | Amaj7 | Amaj7 | Amaj7 |

        | E | E | E | E :‖ *Play 4 times to fade*

Percussion Gun

Words & Music by
Stephen Patterson, Gregory Roberts, Alex Even,
Matthew Clark, Jamie Levinson & Adam Russell

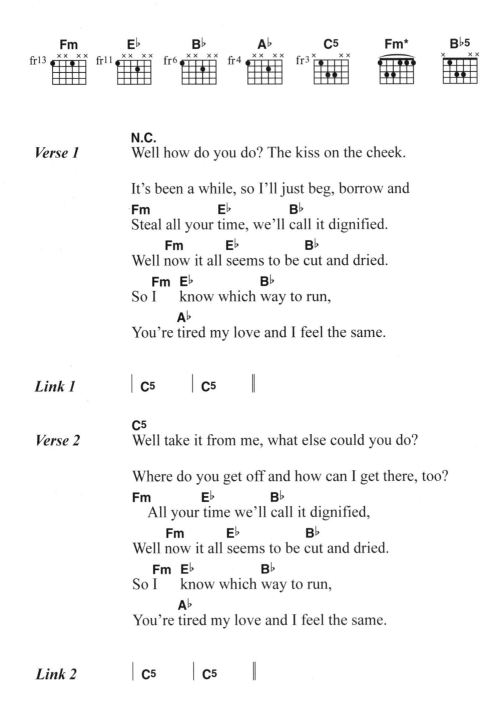

Verse 1

N.C.
Well how do you do? The kiss on the cheek.

It's been a while, so I'll just beg, borrow and
Fm   E♭   B♭
Steal all your time, we'll call it dignified.
    Fm   E♭   B♭
Well now it all seems to be cut and dried.
     Fm E♭   B♭
So I   know which way to run,
           A♭
You're tired my love and I feel the same.

Link 1 | C5 | C5   ‖

Verse 2

C5
Well take it from me, what else could you do?

Where do you get off and how can I get there, too?
Fm   E♭   B♭
  All your time we'll call it dignified,
     Fm   E♭   B♭
Well now it all seems to be cut and dried.
     Fm E♭   B♭
So I   know which way to run,
         A♭
You're tired my love and I feel the same.

Link 2 | C5 | C5   ‖

Verse 3

Fm E♭ B♭
Ooh._____

              Fm   E♭
You'll never   come back,

    B♭
My God can't you see that

Fm E♭   B♭
I   know which way to run,

        A♭
You're tired my love and I feel the same,

     Fm*
The Lebanon won't speak my name now.

Link 3

| C5 | C5 | C5 | ‖

Bridge

Fm E♭ B♭
Ooh._____

Fm E♭ B♭
Ooh._____

Fm E♭ B♭
Ooh._____

Link 4

| B♭5 | B♭5 | B♭5 | ‖

Verse 4

     Fm   E♭   B♭
Now everyone seen rise and shine

   Fm   E♭   B♭
It might not be true, it makes this fine.

      Fm E♭   B♭
'Cause I   know which way to run,

      A♭
You're tired my love and I feel the same,

    Fm*
The Lebanon won't speak my name.

     A♭
Now even rats would jump this ship

B♭
  Oh, just give me some peace of mind,

      Fm E♭ B♭
'Cause I.

Fm E♭ B♭
Ooh._____

Outro

| Fm E♭ | B♭ | C5 | C5 | C5 | C5 | ‖

Papillon

Words & Music by
Tom Smith, Russell Leetch, Christopher Urbanowicz & Edward Lay

Em   G   Bm   C   D

Intro
‖: Em | G Bm | Em | G Bm :‖

Verse 1

Em   G   Bm   Em G Bm
   Make your escape,   you're my own Papil - lon,

Em   G   Bm   Em G Bm
  The world turns too fast,   feel love be - fore it's gone.

   Em   G Bm Em G Bm
It kicks like a sleep twitch,

  Em   G Bm   Em G Bm
  My Papillon,   feel love when it's shone.

Pre-chorus 1

Em G Bm Em G Bm Em G Bm Em
Ah._____

N.C.
It kicks like a sleep twitch.

Link 1
‖: Em | G Bm | Em | G Bm :‖

Chorus 1

C   G   D
Darling, just don't put down your guns yet,

    G   C
If there really was a God here,

    G   D
He'd have raised a hand by now.

G   C   G   D
  Now darling, you're born, get old and die here,

     G   C
Well that's quite enough for me,

     G   D
We'll find our own way home somehow.

Link 2 ‖: Em | G Bm | Em | G Bm :‖

Verse 2

Em | G Bm | Em G Bm
   No sense of doubt   for what you could a - chieve,

Em | G | Bm | Em G
   Well, I found you out,   I've seen the life you wish to leave.

Bm | Em | G Bm Em G Bm
   But when it kicks like a sleep twitch,

Em | G | Bm | Em G Bm
   You will choke,   choke on the air you try to breathe.

Pre-chorus 2   As Pre-chorus 1

Link 3 ‖: Em | G Bm | Em | G Bm :‖

Chorus 2

C | G | D
Darling, just don't put down your guns yet,

   G | C
If there really was a God here,

   G | D
He'd have raised a hand by now.

G C | G | D
   Darling, you're born, get old and die here,

   G | C
Well that's quite enough for me dear,

   G | D | (Em)
We'll find our own way home somehow, how, how.

Bridge ‖: Em | G Bm | Em | G Bm :‖

   Em | G Bm Em G Bm
It kicks like a sleep twitch.

   Em | G Bm Em G Bm
It kicks like a sleep twitch.

Chorus 3

       C   G   D
Darling, just don't put down your guns yet,

           G   C
If there really was a God here,

           G   D
He'd have raised a hand by now.

G C   G   D
    Darling, oh you're born, get old and die here,

           G   C
Well that's quite enough for me, dear

              G   D
We'll find our own way home somehow,

     N.C.
It kicks like a sleep twitch.

Outro

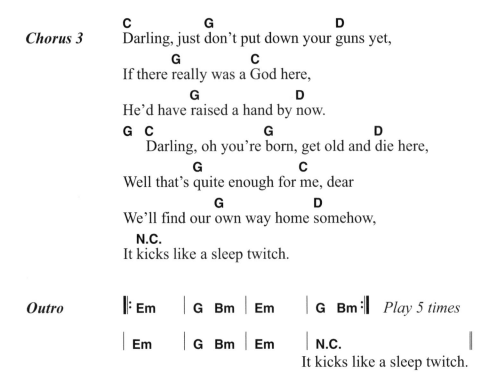

| **‖: Em** | G Bm | Em | G Bm :‖ | *Play 5 times* |

| Em | G Bm | Em | N.C. | ‖ |

It kicks like a sleep twitch.

Rabbit Heart (Raise It Up)

Words & Music by
Florence Welch, Paul Epworth, Joshua Deutsch,
Brian Degraw, Elizabeth Bougatsos & Timothy Dewit

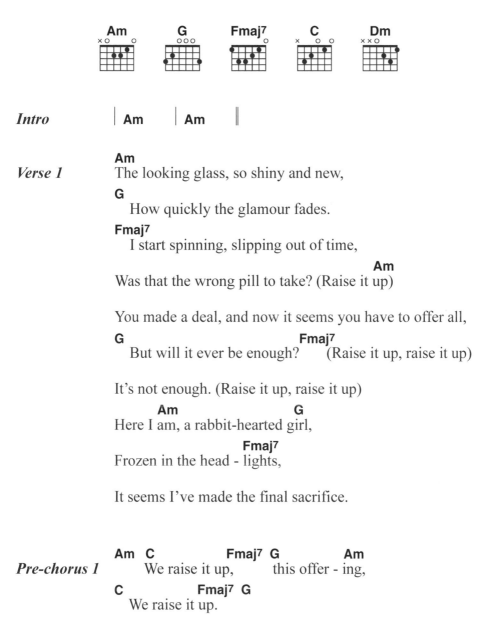

| Am | G | Fmaj7 | C | Dm |

Intro | Am | Am |

Verse 1

Am
The looking glass, so shiny and new,
G
How quickly the glamour fades.
Fmaj7
I start spinning, slipping out of time,
                                        Am
Was that the wrong pill to take? (Raise it up)

You made a deal, and now it seems you have to offer all,
G   **Fmaj7**
   But will it ever be enough?   (Raise it up, raise it up)

It's not enough. (Raise it up, raise it up)
       Am   **G**
Here I am, a rabbit-hearted girl,
               Fmaj7
Frozen in the head - lights,

It seems I've made the final sacrifice.

Am **C**   **Fmaj7** **G**   **Am**
Pre-chorus 1   We raise it up,   this offer - ing,
C   **Fmaj7** **G**
   We raise it up.

Chorus 1

(G)   **Dm**   **Fmaj7**
This is a gift, it comes with a price,

           Am   **G**
Who is the lamb and who is the knife?

             Dm   **Fmaj7**
And Midas is king and he holds me so tight

            Am   **G**
And turns me to gold in the sun - light.

Verse 2

Am   **G**
  I look around, but I can't find you, (Raise it up)

                            Fmaj7
If only I could see your face. (Raise it up)

I start rushing towards the skyline, (Raise it up)

I wish that I could just be brave.

           Am   **G**
I must be - come a lion-hearted girl,

           Fmaj7
Ready for a fight,

Before I make the final sacrifice.

Pre-chorus 2   As Pre-chorus 1

Chorus 2   As Chorus 1

Bridge

N.C.(Am)
Raise it up, raise it up,

Raise it up, raise it up.

           Dm   **Fmaj7**
And in the spring I shed my skin

             Am   **G**
And it blows a - way with the changing winds.

           Dm   **Fmaj7**
The waters turn from blue to red

             Am   **G**
As towards the sky I offer it.

Chorus 3	As Chorus 1
Chorus 4	As Chorus 1

Chorus 5

(G)   **Dm**   **Fmaj⁷**
This is a gift, it comes with a price,

        Am   **G**
Who is the lamb and who is the knife?

        Dm   **Fmaj⁷**
Midas is king and he holds me so tight

          G
And turns me to gold in the sunlight.

        Am
This is a gift.

The Reeling

Words & Music by
Michael Angelakos

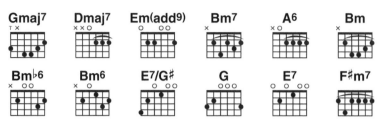

Capo first fret

Intro ‖: Gmaj⁷ | Gmaj⁷ | Dmaj⁷ | Dmaj⁷ :‖ *Play 4 times*

‖: Em(add9) | Gmaj⁷ | Bm⁷ | A⁶ :‖

Verse 1

Em(add9)   Gmaj⁷   Bm⁷
   We dug these holes we crawled into,

          A⁶
Now they're my home.

Em(add9)   Gmaj⁷   Bm⁷
   Now here I cannot feel the wind,

        A⁶
Can't feel the rain all cold.

Em(add9)   Gmaj⁷   Bm⁷
   And I be - lieve in gentle harmony,

        A⁶
Well how I loathe all this obscenity.

Em(add9)   Gmaj⁷   Bm⁷
   Is this the way my life has got to be?

     A⁶
By a single opportunity.

Chorus 1

Gmaj⁷
Look at me, oh look at me, is this the way I've always been?

   Dmaj⁷
Oh no, oh no.

Gmaj⁷
Now I'm dreaming somebody would simply come and kidnap me.

   Dmaj⁷
Oh no, oh no.

Gmaj⁷
Everyday I lie awake and pray to God today's the day.

cont.

Dmaj7
Oh no, oh no.

Gmaj7
Here I am, oh here I am, oh when will someone understand?

Dmaj7
Oh no, oh no.

Link

‖: **Em(add9)** | **Gmaj7** | **Bm7** | **A6** :‖

Verse 2

Em(add9)   **Gmaj7**   **Bm7**
  And all at once I feel this,

                A6
Oh how it clings to me.

Em(add9)   **Gmaj7**   **Bm7**
  It reels and calls me towards it,

                A6
Confounding destiny.

Em(add9)   **Gmaj7**   **Bm7**
  And I can feel the magnets pinch my hands,

            A6   **Em(add9)**
The more I run the more I am convinced.

            Gmaj7   **Bm7**
A girl who loves is like a precious glimpse,

            A6
Just like we settle in the foggy mist.

Chorus 2   As Chorus 1

Instrumental | **Bm** | **Bm Bm♭6** | **Bm6** | **Bm♭6** | **E7/G♯** |
| **G** | **E7** | **G** | **E7** | **G** ‖

Chorus 3   As Chorus 1

Outro   ‖: **Bm7** | **Bm7** | **F♯m7** | **F♯m7** :‖ *Repeat to fade*

169

Revelry

Words & Music by
Caleb Followill, Nathan Followill,
Jared Followill & Matthew Followill

Verse 1

E5
What a night for a dance, you know I'm a dancing ma - chine
F#5/E

G#5/E
With a fire in my bones and the sweet taste of kero - sene.
F#5/E

E5
I get lost in the night so high I don't want to come down
F#5/E

G#5/E
To face the loss of the good thing that I've found.
F#5/E

Link 1

E5   F#5/E
Whoo, hoo, hoo.

G#5/E   F#5/E
Whoo, hoo, hoo.

Verse 2

E5
In the dark of the night I could hear you calling my name,
F#5/E

G#5/E
With the harvest of hearts I still feel full of pain.
F#5/E

E5
So I drink and I smoke and I ask you if you're ever around,
F#5/E

G#5/E
Even though it was me who drove us right in the ground.
F#5/E

Chorus 1

A(add9)
See the time we shared it was precious to me,

B(add)11   E
But all the while I was dreaming of revel - ry.

F#m11   G#m♭6   F#m11
Ooh,_____   ooh._____

Verse 3

E   F$\sharp$5/E
Gonna run, baby run like a stream down a mountain - side
      G$\sharp$5/E   F$\sharp$5/E
With the wind in my back I don't ever even bat an eye.
    E   F$\sharp$5/E
Just know it was you all along who had a hold of my heart,
    G$\sharp$5/E   F$\sharp$5/E
But the demon and me were the best of friends from the start.

Chorus 2

    A(add9)
So the time we shared it was precious to me,
          B(add)11   E
All the while I was dreaming of revel - ry.
  F$\sharp$m11 G$\sharp$m$\flat$6   F$\sharp$m11
Ooh,_____   ooh._____
           E
Dreaming of revel - ry.
  F$\sharp$m11 G$\sharp$m$\flat$6   F$\sharp$m11
Ooh,_____   ooh._____

Verse 4

    E
And I told myself: "Boy, away you go."
  F$\sharp$m11
It rained so hard it felt like snow,
G$\sharp$m$\flat$6   F$\sharp$m11
Everything came tumbling down on me.
    E
In the back of the woods, in the dark of the night,
F$\sharp$m11
Paleness of the old moonlight,
G$\sharp$m$\flat$6   F$\sharp$m11
Everything just felt so incom - plete.

Outro

          E   F$\sharp$m11
Dreaming of revel - ry. Ooh,_____
              G$\sharp$m$\flat$6   F$\sharp$m11
Dreaming of revelry.   Ooh,_____
          E   F$\sharp$m11
Dreaming of revel - ry. Ooh,_____
              G$\sharp$m$\flat$6   F$\sharp$m11
Dreaming of revelry.   Ooh._____

The Road

Words & Music by
Frank Turner

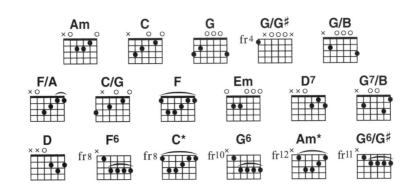

Chorus 1

Am   C
To the east, to the east,

G   G/G♯   Am
The road be - neath my feet.

Am   C
To the west, to the west,

G   G/G♯   Am
But I haven't got there yet.

G/B C   G/B
And to the north, to the north,

F/A   C
  Never to be caught.

F   C
To the south, to the south,

G   G/G♯   Am
My time is running out.

Link 1 | Am | Am   ‖

Verse 1

Am   Em   F   G
Ever since my childhood I've been scared, I've been a - fraid

C   G/B   F   D7
Of being trapped by circumstance and staying in one place.

Am   Em   F   G
So I always keep a small bag full of clothes carefully stored,

C   G/B   F   Em Am
Somewhere secret, somewhere safe and somewhere close to the door.

Link 2 | Am | Am   ‖

Verse 2
```
Am                      Em                      F        G
```
Well I've travelled many countries, I've washed my feet in many seas,
```
          C        G/B           F           D7
```
I've drunk with drifters in Vienna and with punks in old D.C.
```
          Am      Em        F       G
```
And I've driven across deserts driven by the iro - ny
```
          C            G/B              F      Em   Am
```
That only being shackled to the the road could ever I be free.

Chorus 2   As Chorus 1

Verse 3
```
Am                      Em              F           G
```
I've felt old before my time but now I keep the age a - way
```
   C          G/B                F          D7
```
By burning up the miles and yeah, by filling up my days.
```
       Am              Em                  F          G
```
And the nights, a thousand nights I've played, a thousand more to go
```
          C              G/B              F      Em      Am
```
Before I take a breath and steal myself for the next one thousand shows.

Chorus 3   As Chorus 1

Instrumental | Am   Em | F   G | C   G7/B | F   D |

   | Am   Em | F   G | C   G7/B | F   D   ‖

Bridge
```
(D)      Am              Em          F               G
```
Yeah, so saddle up your hor - ses now and keep your powder dry,
```
        C            G7/B           F              D
```
'Cause the truth is you won't be here long, yeah, soon you're gonna die.
```
       Am          Em            F          G
```
To the heart, to the heart, there's no time for you to waste,
```
        C            G7/B            F          D
```
You won't find your precious answers now by staying in one place.
```
       F         D      G
```
Yeah, by giving up the chase.

Chorus 3

  (G) **Am**   **C**
To the east, to the east,

   G **G/G♯** **Am**
The road be - neath my feet.

    Am   **C**
To the west, to the west,

   G **G/G♯** **Am**
But I haven't got there yet.

   G/B **C**   **G/B**
And to the north, to the north,

    F/A   **C**
Well I never will be caught.

    F   **C**
To the south, to the south,

   G **G/G♯** **Am**
My time is running out.

      F   **C**
Yeah, to the south to the south,

   G **G/G♯** **Am**
My time is running out.

      F   **C**
Yeah, to the south to the south,

   G **G/G♯** **Am**
My time is running out.

Outro

F6   **C*** **G6**   **Am***
 I face the hori - zon, everywhere I go,

F6   **C***   **G6**   **Am***
 I face the hori - zon, the horizon is my home.

F6   **C*** **G6**   **Am***
 I face the hori - zon, everywhere that I go,

F6   **C*** **G6**   **G6/G♯** **Am***
 I face the hori - zon, the horizon is my home.

She Said

Words & Music by
Benjamin Ballance-Drew, Eric Appapoulay,
Richard Cassell & Tom Goss

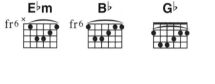

Intro | E♭m | E♭m | E♭m | E♭m ‖

Verse 1

E♭m
She said, "I love you boy, I love you so."

                                            B♭
She said, "I love you baby oh, oh, oh, oh,   oh."

E♭m
  She said, "I love you more than words can say."

                                          B♭
She said, "I love you bay - ay - ay - ay - ay - by."

Link 1 | E♭m | E♭m | E♭m | E♭m ‖

Verse 2

E♭m
  So I said, "What you sayin' girl, it can't be right,
B♭
  How can you be in love with me?

We only just met tonight."
E♭m
  So she said, "Boy, I loved you from the start,
B♭
  When I first heard 'Love Goes Down',

Something started burning in my heart."
G♭   B♭
  I said, "Stop this crazy talk,
G♭   B♭
  And leave right now and close the door."

E♭m
She said, "But I love you boy, I love you so."

B♭
She said, "I love you baby oh, oh, oh, oh,   oh."

E♭m
    She said, "I love you more than words can say."

B♭
    She said, "I love you bay - ay - ay - ay - ay - by."

Yes she did.

Rap

E♭m
    So now I'm up in the courts

Pleading my case from the witness box,

Telling the judge and the jury

The same thing that I said to the cops.

B♭
    On the day that I got arrested

"I'm innocent." I protested,

She just feels rejected,

Had her heart broken by someone she's obsessed with.

E♭m
    'Cause she likes the sound of my music,

Which makes her a fan of my music.

'S'why 'Love Goes Down' makes her lose it,

'Cause she can't seperate the man from the music.

B♭
    And I'm saying all this in the stand,

While my girl cries tears from the gallery.

This has got bigger than I ever could have planned,

Like that song by The Zutons, 'Valerie'.

G♭
    'Cept the jury don't look like they're buying it,

This is making me nervous.

cont.

B♭

Arms crossed, screwed faced like I'm trying it,

Their eyes fixed on me like I'm murderous,

G♭

They wanna lock me up

And throw away the key.

B♭

They wanna send me down,

Even though I told them she...

Link 2 | E♭m | E♭m | E♭m | E♭m   ‖

Verse 3

E♭m

She said, "I love you boy, I love you so."

B♭

She said, "I love you baby oh, oh, oh, oh,   oh."

Yes she did.

E♭m

She said, "I love you more than words can say."

B♭

She said, "I love you bay - ay - ay - ay - ay - by."

E♭m

So I said, "Then why the hell you gotta treat me this way?

You don't know what love is,

B♭

You wouldn't do this if you   did."

E♭m

No, no, no, no, oh.

Skinny Little Bitch

Words & Music by
Courtney Love & Micko Larkin

F#5   A5   E5   B5   D5   fr5

Verse 1

N.C. F#5
Skinny little bitch

A5 F#5
Star - ing at the mirror

A5 F#5 A5 F#5
In your desperation to dis - appear.

A5 F#5 A5 F#5
And you would be oh so dumb to fuck with me,

A5 F#5 A5 F#5
'Cause ba - by you're much too young to end up with me.

Chorus 1

F#5 E5 B5 F#5
Your bedroom walls are falling down

E5 B5 F#5
And every - one can see you now.

E5 B5 F#5
Your bedroom walls, they sell for cheap,

E5
You lie, you lie alone,

F#5
You lie alone, you never sleep,

A5 F#5
Oh, you never sleep.

Verse 1

N.C.   F♯5
Skinny little bitch

A5   F♯5
Pray - ing to the Lord,

A5   F♯5   A5 F♯5
Pray - ing for some salvation 'cause she's oh so bored.

A5 F♯5   A5   F♯5
In my vile sex horror and   my cheap drugs hell,

A5 F♯5   A5   F♯5
I am all the things you'll nev - er   live to tell.

Chorus 2

F♯5   E5   B5   F♯5
And you will never see the light,

E5   B5   F♯5
I'll just ob - scure it out of spite.

E5   B5   F♯5
You're just a nasty piece of work,

E5
Come on, come on baby,

F♯5
Come on baby, let it burn,

A5 F♯5
Oh, baby, does it   hurt?

Bridge

B5   D5
Born of foul crea - tion,

B5   D5   E5
Born of sour milk, cocaine filth.

Chorus 3

F♯5   E5   B5   F♯5
You staggered here on broken glass,

E5   B5   F♯5
So I could kick your scrawny ass.

E5   B5   F♯5
All the drugs and all the burns,

E5   F♯5
What a nasty, what a nasty, nasty piece of work.

A5 F♯5
Oh, baby, does it   hurt?

A5   F♯5
Oh, baby, just go slow - er,

A5   F♯5
Oh, baby, just go low - er.

Outro

𝄆   A5   F♯5
Skinny little bitch. 𝄇 *Play 9 times*

Sometime Around Midnight

Words & Music by
Mikel Jollett

Am   F   C   Csus4   Csus2   Fmaj7   G

Capo third fret

Intro   ‖: Am │ F │ C │ C :‖ *Play 3 times*

│ C Csus4 │ C Csus2 │ C Csus4 │ C Csus2 │

│ Am │ Fmaj7 │ C Csus4 │ C Csus2 ‖

Verse 1

(Csus2) C   Csus4 C   Csus2   C   Csus4 C
And it   starts   some - time around midnight,

Csus2   Am   Fmaj7
  Or at least that's when you lose your - self

                    C   Csus4 C
For a minute or two.

Csus2   C   Csus4 C Csus2   C   Csus4 C
  As you stand   under the bar lights,

Csus2   Am
  And the band plays some song

                 Fmaj7   C   Csus4 C
About forget - ting yourself for a while.

Csus2   Am   Fmaj7   C   Csus4 C
  And the pi - ano's this melancholy soundtrack to her smile

Csus2   Am
  In that white dress she's wearing

           Fmaj7   (C)
You haven't seen her for a while.

Link 1   │ C Csus4 │ C Csus2 │ C Csus4 │ C Csus2 ‖

Verse 2

(Csus2) C   Csus4 C Csus2   C   Csus4 C
But you know   that she's watching,

Csus2 Am
  She's laughing, she's turning,

      Fmaj7   C   Csus4 C
She's holding her tonic like a cross.

Csus2   Am
  The room suddenly spinning,

                  C   Csus4 C
She walks up and asks how you are.

Csus2   Am   (C)
  So you can smell her perfume,

      Fmaj7   (C)
You can see her lying naked in your arms.

Link 2 | C Csus4 | C Csus2 | C Csus4 | C Csus2 ‖

Verse 3

(Csus2)   C   Csus4 C Csus2   C   Csus4 C
And so there's a change   in your e - motions,

Csus2   Am
  And all these memories come rushing

      Fmaj7   C   Csus4 C
Like feral waves to your mind,

Csus2 Am
  Of the curl of your bodies

      Fmaj7   C   Csus4 C
Like two   perfect circles en - twined.

Csus2   Am
  And you feel hopeless, and homeless

      Fmaj7   (C)
And lost in the haze of the wine.

Link 3 | C Csus4 | C Csus2 | C Csus4 | C Csus2 ‖

Verse 4

(Csus2)   C Csus4 C   Csus2   C   Csus4 C
Then she leaves   with someone you don't know

Csus2 Am
  But she makes sure you saw her,

      Fmaj7   C   Csus4 C
She looks right at you and bolts.

Csus2 Am
  As she walks out the door,

cont.
            Fmaj7   **C**   **Csus4 C**
Your blood boiling, your stomach in ropes.

Csus2   **Am**
And when your friends say, "What is it?"

    Fmaj7   **(C)**
You look like you've seen a ghost.

Bridge

C	C	C	C	
F	G	Am	Am	
F	G	C Csus4	C Csus2	C Csus4	C Csus2

Verse 5

(Csus2) **C**   **Csus4 C Csus2**   **C**   **Csus4 C**
Then you walk   under the streetlights,

Csus2   **Am**
And you're too drunk to notice

    Fmaj7   **C**   **Csus4 C**
That everyone is staring at you.

Csus2   **Am**
You just don't care what you look like,

    Fmaj7   **C**   **Csus4 C**
The world is falling around you.

    Am
You just have to see her,

    F
You just have to see her,

    C
You just have to see her,

    Am
You just have to see her,

    F
You just have to see her,

                    (C)
You know that she'll break you in two.

Outro

C	C	C	C	
:‖ Am	F	C	C	‖: *Play 3 times*
C	C	C	C	
Am	F	C	C	‖

Starry Eyed

Words & Music by
Ellie Goulding & Jonny Lattimer

Em7   Dsus2   Am7   G   Bm7   fr2   C6   C(add9)

Capo first fret

Intro

Em7   Dsus2
Oh, oh,   starry eyed,

Am7   G
Oh, oh,   star-ar-ar-ar.

Em7   Dsus2   Am7   G
Oh, oh, (deye yrrats,   deye yrrats),   starry eyed,

Em7
Hit, hit, hit, hit, hit me with lightning.

Verse 1

Em7   Dsus2   Am7   G
Handle-bars, never let go, let go for anyone.

Em7   Dsus2   Am7   G
Take me in and   throw out my heart and get a new one.

Bm7   Em7
Next thing we're touching,

G   C6
You look at me it's like you hit me with lightning, ah.

Chorus 1

Em7   Dsus2   Am7   G
Oh,   everybody's starry eyed

Em7
And everybody glows.

Dsus2   Am7   G
Oh,   everybody's starry eyed

Em7
And my body goes,

Dsus2
A-whoa, oh, oh, ah, ah.

Am7   G
A-whoa, oh, oh, ah, ah.

Em7   Dsus2   Am7   G
A-whoa, oh, oh.

Verse 2

Em7   Dsus2   Am7   G
    So we burst into colours, co - lours and carousels,

Em7   Dsus2   Am7   G
    Fall head first like paper planes and playground games.

Bm7   Em7
    Next thing we're touching,

    G   C6
You look at me it's like you hit me with lightning, ah.

Chorus 2

Em7 Dsus2   Am7   G
    Oh,   everybody's starry eyed

                Em7
And everybody glows.

     Dsus2   Am7   G
Oh,   everybody's starry eyed

             Em7
And my body goes,

       Dsus2
A-whoa, oh, oh, a-whoa, whoa, whoa, whoa.

Am7   G
    A-whoa, oh, oh, ah, ah.

Em7   Dsus2
    A-whoa, oh, oh, a-whoa, whoa, whoa, whoa.

Am7   G
No, no, no, no.

Bridge

Em7
    Next thing we're touching,

C(add9)
    Next thing we're touching,

Bm7
    Next thing we're touching,

Am7
    Next thing we're touching,

Em7
    Next thing we're touching,

C(add9)
    Next thing we're touching,

Bm7
    Next thing we're touching,

Am7
    Next thing we're touching,

Em7
Hit me with lightning.

Chorus 3

Em7 Dsus2   Am7   G
   Oh,   everybody's starry eyed

          Em7
And everybody glows.

    Dsus2   Am7   G
Oh,   everybody's starry eyed

          Em7   N.C.
And my body goes.

    Dsus2   Am7   G
Oh,   everybody's starry eyed

          Em7
And everybody glows.

    Dsus2   Am7   G
Oh,   everybody's starry eyed

          Em7
And my body goes,

        Dsus2
A-whoa, oh, oh, ah, ah.

Am7   G
  A-whoa, oh, oh,

          Em7   Dsus2
Oh, oh and my body goes,

Am7   (G)
  Oh, oh, oh.

Standing On The Shore

Words & Music by
Luke Steele, Nick Littlemore & Peter Mayes

Bm   Bm/D   Gmaj7   Bm/E   Am7   D

Intro

‖: Bm | Bm | Bm | Bm :‖

‖: Bm | Bm/D | Gmaj7 | Bm/E :‖

Verse 1

Bm   Bm/D
Standing on the shore,

Gmaj7   Bm/E
Waiting for the ship in call,

     Bm   Bm/D
There's something in the way I move

             Gmaj7   Bm/E
That keeps them on their own.

     Bm   Bm/D
The star explodes a storm,

         Gmaj7   Bm/E
A billion seasons born,

   Bm   Bm/D
A shock to the waves I know,

         Gmaj7   Bm/E
Breaking far from shore.

Chorus 1

Am7   D   Am7   D
       Don't want to talk,

      Am7   D
All I hear is noise,

      Am7   D
Don't want to talk.

Verse 2

    Bm   **Bm/D**
The future's in my hands,

  Gmaj7   **Bm/E**
I hold it in my palms,

    Bm
En - grave it in the ley lines

Bm/D   **Gmaj7** **Bm/E**
Running right down her arms.

Bm   **Bm/D**
Speak in silent tongues,

Gmaj7   **Bm/E**
Lies reflect the times,

    Bm
The ghosts and the shadows

Bm/D   **Gmaj7** **Bm/E**
Fill the living scene.

Chorus 2   As Chorus 1

Chorus 3   As Chorus 1

Instrumental ‖: Bm | Bm | Bm | Bm :‖ *Play 4 times*

                ‖: Bm | Bm/D | Gmaj7 | Bm/E :‖ *Play 4 times*

Chorus 4   As Chorus 1

Chorus 5   As Chorus 1

Outro   ‖: Bm | Bm/D | Gmaj7 | Bm/E :‖ *Repeat to fade*

Plan B

Stay Too Long

Words & Music by
Benjamin Ballance-Drew, Eric Appapoulay, Richard Cassell & Tom Goss

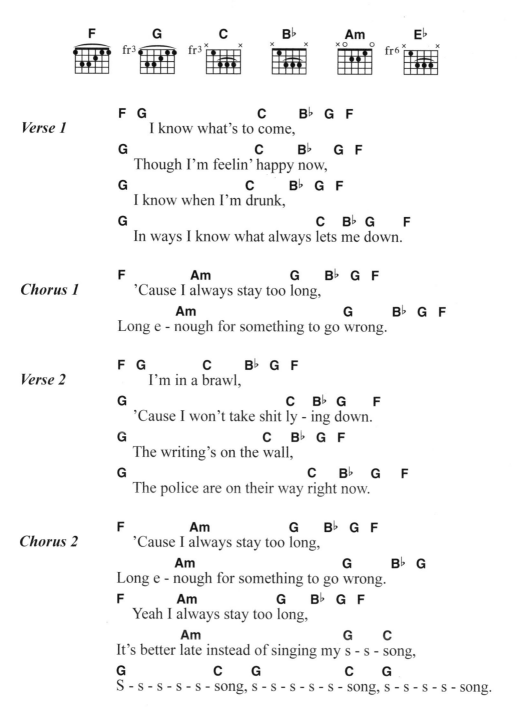

Verse 1

F G   C Bb G F
  I know what's to come,

G   C Bb G F
  Though I'm feelin' happy now,

G   C Bb G F
  I know when I'm drunk,

G   C Bb G F
  In ways I know what always lets me down.

Chorus 1

F   Am   G Bb G F
  'Cause I always stay too long,

     Am   G Bb G F
  Long e - nough for something to go wrong.

Verse 2

F G C Bb G F
  I'm in a brawl,

G   C Bb G F
  'Cause I won't take shit ly - ing down.

G   C Bb G F
  The writing's on the wall,

G   C Bb G F
  The police are on their way right now.

Chorus 2

F   Am   G Bb G F
  'Cause I always stay too long,

     Am   G Bb G
  Long e - nough for something to go wrong.

F   Am   G Bb G F
  Yeah I always stay too long,

     Am   G C
  It's better late instead of singing my s - s - song,

G   C G   C G
  S - s - s - s - s - song, s - s - s - s - s - song, s - s - s - s - s - song.

Rap 1

N.C.   F   G
I've got my peeps there with me shouting: "Pull up your socks."
      F G
'Cause we just broke the law and now we're running from cops.
       F G
I got my lip bust fighting, now there's blood on my top
      F   G
And I'm still out looking for a party, somewhere to stop.
       F   G
I've got my peeps then tellin' me they know where it's at,
      F   G
So I pull out twenty notes and jump straight into a cab.
       F   G
I'm on my way to where I'm going thinkin' I need more Jack,
     F   G
But that probably ain't the brightest idea I've ever had,

'Cause...

Chorus 3

F   Am   G
I always stay too long,
F   Am   G
Long e - nough for something to go wrong.

(Hey!)

Verse 3

F G   C   B♭ G F
   On a run from the law,
G   C B♭ G F
I'm lookin' worse for wear.
G   C   B♭ G F
I go through a door,
G   C B♭   G   F
And suddenly I find my - self some - where.

Chorus 4

F Am   G   C B♭ G F
  Something's bound to go wrong,
Am   G   C B♭ G F
If I stay too long,
 Am   G   C B♭ G F
I know I'm gotta get to dawn_____
   Am   G   C   G   C
Be - fore I start singin' my s - s - song, s - s - song,
G   C   G   C   G   C
S - s - s - s - s - song, s - s - s - s - s - song, s - s - s - s - s - song,
G   C   G   C   G
  S - s - song, s - s - s - s - s - song,   song, song.

Bridge

    F G B♭ E♭ B♭   F   G B♭ E♭ B♭
                Ah c' - mon,

       F   G B♭ E♭ B♭
Ah c' - mon,

       F   G   B♭   E♭   B♭
Ah c' - mon, c'mon, c'mon, c'mon.

Rap 2

(B♭)   F   G   B♭   E♭   B♭
I've got my peeps then with me at the bar doing shots,

          F   G   B♭   E♭   B♭
'Cause now we're so fucking plastered we don't know when to stop.

          F   G   B♭   E♭   B♭
I've got my girl - friend ringing me, belling me up,

       F   G   B♭   E♭   B♭
I know I should prob'ly answer but I just can't be fucked.

       F   G   B♭ E♭   B♭
I've got my peeps then with me and I'm havin' a blast,

       F G   B♭   E♭ B♭
I'm feeling so fucking good right now, I want it to last.

    F   G   B♭   E♭   B♭
So I put my 'phone on silent and I re - fill my glass,

          F G   B♭   E♭   B♭
The music's so fucking banging, feel like I wanna dance.

        F   G B♭   E♭   B♭
I'm at the bar and I see a chick checking me out,

       F G   B♭   E♭   B♭
From a - far yeah, she wants my dick there ain't a doubt.

       F   G   B♭   E♭   B♭
She's got a skirt so short, it makes you drool from the mouth,

F   G   B♭   E♭   B♭
Look - ing my way as if to say I'm in with a shout.

     F   G   B♭   E♭   B♭
So I pull a chair over there and buy her a drink,

F   G   B♭   E♭   B♭
She says "Cheers." I say "Yeah." our glasses go clink.

      F   G B♭   E♭   B♭
Now I'm being bad in a cab rubbing this girl,

      F   G   B♭   E♭   B♭
Once the cab is paid we make our way up to the ho - tel.

      F   G B♭   E♭   B♭
Now I'm in the lift, getting lips, go nice and slow,

    F G   B♭ E♭   B♭
But do I care? Do I fuck! I'm on a roll, yo!

F G B♭ E♭ B♭
      Ah!

Sweet Disposition

Words & Music by
Lorenzo Sillitto & Abby Mandagi

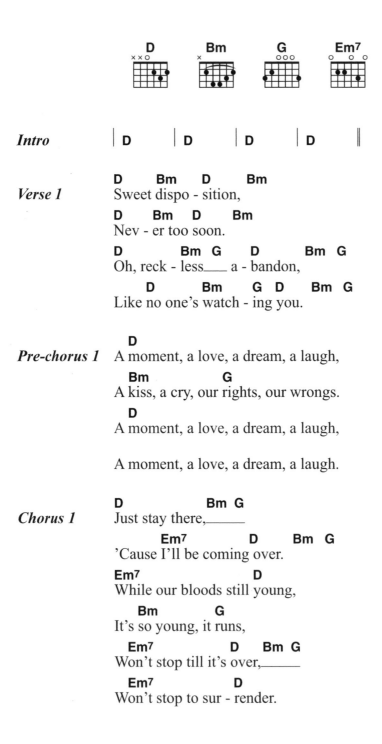

Intro | D | D | D | D |

Verse 1

D   Bm   D   Bm
Sweet dispo - sition,

D   Bm   D   Bm
Nev - er too soon.

D   Bm G   D   Bm G
Oh, reck - less____ a - bandon,

        D   Bm   G D Bm G
Like no one's watch - ing you.

Pre-chorus 1

        D
A moment, a love, a dream, a laugh,

    Bm   G
A kiss, a cry, our rights, our wrongs.

        D
A moment, a love, a dream, a laugh,

A moment, a love, a dream, a laugh.

Chorus 1

D   Bm G
Just stay there,_____

      Em7   D   Bm G
'Cause I'll be coming over.

Em7   D
While our bloods still young,

    Bm   G
It's so young, it runs,

    Em7   D Bm G
Won't stop till it's over,_____

    Em7   D
Won't stop to sur - render.

Verse 2

D   Bm G   D   Bm G
Songs of   despe - ration,

D Bm   G   D   Bm G
I   played them for you.

Pre-chorus 2

       D
A moment, a love, a dream, a laugh,

A kiss, a cry, our rights, our wrongs.

A moment, a love, a dream, a laugh,

A moment, a love, a dream, a laugh.

Chorus 2

D   Bm G
Just stay there,_____

      Em7   D   Bm   G
'Cause I'll be coming over._____

Em7   D
While our bloods still young,

   Bm   G
It's so young, it runs,

   Em7   D   Bm G
Won't stop till it's over,_____

   Em7   D   Bm   G
Won't stop to sur - render._____

Em7   D   Bm G
Won't stop till it's over._____

Em7   D   Bm G
Won't stop till it's over._____

Em7   D   Bm G
Won't stop till it's over._____

       D
Won't stop to sur - render.

Take Over The World

Words & Music by
Liam Fray

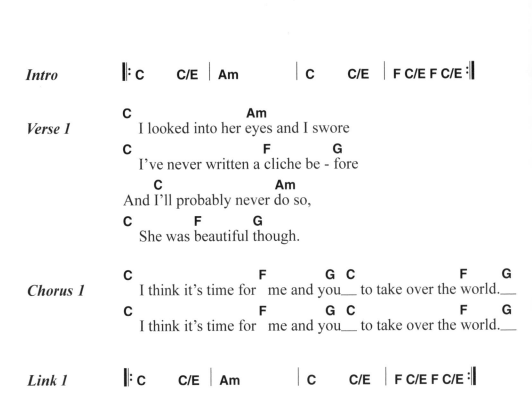

Intro ‖: C   C/E | Am | C   C/E | F C/E F C/E :‖

Verse 1

C   Am
I looked into her eyes and I swore
C   F   G
I've never written a cliche be - fore
        C   Am
And I'll probably never do so,
C   F   G
She was beautiful though.

Chorus 1

C   F   G C   F   G
I think it's time for me and you__ to take over the world.__
C   F   G C   F   G
I think it's time for me and you__ to take over the world.__

Link 1 ‖: C   C/E | Am | C   C/E | F C/E F C/E :‖

Verse 2

        C   Am
I'm only a paper - boy from the North West,

    C   F   G
But I can scrub up well in my Sunday best.

    C   Am
How could I ever do for you?

              C   F   G
Because I'm true and I'm real and this is how I feel.

Chorus 2   As Chorus 1

Link 2   As Link 1

Verse 3

   C   Am   C
A glossy maga - zine on the coffee table,

                 F   G   C
And you've held court with half of the culprits

       Am   C
In there   who seem un - stable,

                      F   G
But you don't look at them   like you do at me.

Chorus 3

   C   F   G   C   F   G   C
Those eyes are only mine,   what a wonderful time,

F   G   C   F   G
When your eyes are mine and mine are yours.

Bridge

Am   E/G♯   G   D/F♯
I turn over in bed and you're not there, nowhere to be seen,

Am   E/G♯   G   D/F♯
All I can do is flip the Mac and gently touch the screen.

      F   G   (C)
Oh,___ oh.____

Link 3

```
         C     C/E Am       C  C/E F  C/E F  C/E
         Oh,_____ oh,____        oh,_____
         C     C/E Am       C  C/E F  C/E F  C/E
         Oh,_____ oh.____
```

Chorus 4

```
         C                        F       G C                  F       G
           I think it's time for  me and you__ to take over the world.__
         C                        F       G C                  F       G
           I think it's time for  me and you__ to take over the world.__
         C         F      G
         Take over the world.
         C         F      G
         Take over the world.__
         C         F      G
         Take over the world.
         C          F     G C
         Take over the world.__
```

Foals

This Orient

Words & Music by
Yannis Philippakis, James Smith,
Jack Bevan, Edwin Congreave & Walter Gervers

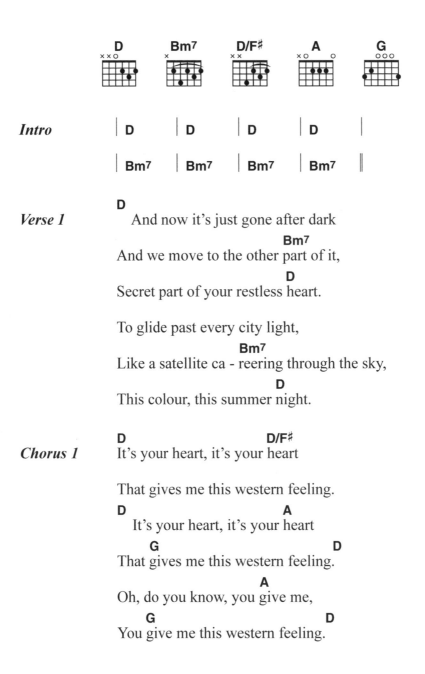

Intro

| D | D | D | D |
| Bm7 | Bm7 | Bm7 | Bm7 |

Verse 1

D
And now it's just gone after dark
                  Bm7
And we move to the other part of it,
          D
Secret part of your restless heart.

To glide past every city light,
           Bm7
Like a satellite ca - reering through the sky,
         D
This colour, this summer night.

Chorus 1

D   D/F♯
It's your heart, it's your heart

That gives me this western feeling.
D   A
It's your heart, it's your heart
    G   D
That gives me this western feeling.
       A
Oh, do you know, you give me,
   G   D
You give me this western feeling.

Verse 2

    D
Now look back, see how far you've come,

         Bm7
Will you unravel in the sun,

         D
Come undone, find your place?

Held up high, said from string as well,

      Bm7
No return to that restless place,

            D
You've reached it, you've found your grace.

Chorus 2   As Chorus 1

Bridge

    D
It's your heart, it's your heart

That gives you this western feeling.

It's your heart, that gives you,

That gives you this western feeling.

Chorus 3

    D   **Bm7**
  It's your heart, that gives you,

                     D
That gives you this western feeling.

         Bm7
It's your heart, it's your heart

                     D
That gives you this western feeling.

          A
Oh, do you know what gives me,

    G   **D**
And it gives me this western feeling.

         A
Oh, do you know what gives me,

    G   **D**
What gives me this western feeling.

Tighten Up

Words & Music by
Daniel Auerbach & Patrick Carney

F♯m fr9 **Amaj7** fr7 **Bm** fr7 **C♯7** fr4 **C♯m7** fr9 **A** fr5 **B** fr7

Intro

‖: F♯m | Amaj7 | Bm | C♯7 :‖

Verse 1

     F♯m   Amaj7
I wanted love, I needed love,

   Bm   C♯7
Most of all, most of all.

   F♯m   Amaj7
Someone said true   love was dead

       Bm   C♯7   F♯m
And I'm bound to fall, bound to fall for you.

Amaj7   Bm   C♯7
Oh, what can I do? Yeah.

Verse 2

     F♯m   Amaj7
Take my badge but my heart remains

      Bm   C♯7
Lov - ing you, ba - by child.

    F♯m   Amaj7
Tighten up on   your reigns,

      Bm   C♯7   F♯m
You're running wild, run - ning wild, it's true.

Link 1

‖: F♯m | C♯m7 | F♯m | C♯m7 |

| F♯m | C♯m7 | A | B :‖

Verse 3

F#m   Amaj7
Sick for days, so   many ways

    Bm   C#7
I'm aching now, I'm aching now.

    F#m   Amaj7
It's times like these, I need relief,

    Bm   C#7
Please show me how, oh, show me how

    F#m Amaj7   Bm   C#7
To get right,   yes, out of   sight.

Verse 4

    F#m   Amaj7
When I was young and moving fast,

    Bm   C#7
Nothing slowed me down, oh, slowed me down.

F#m   Amaj7
Now I let the others pass,

    Bm   C#7
I've come around, oh, come around,

        F#m
'Cause I've found.

Link 2

‖: F#m | C#m7 | F#m | C#m7 |

| F#m | C#m7 | A | B :‖ F#m ‖

Bridge

| F#m | C#m7 | F#m | C#m7 |

| F#m | C#m7 | A | B |

F#7   C#m7   F#m   C#m7
Living just to keep going, going just to be sane.

F#7   C#m7   A B
All the while I know it's   such a shame.

F#7   C#m7   F#m   C#m7
I don't need to get steady, I know just how I feel.

F#7   C#m7   A B
Telling you to be ready   my dear.

Outro

‖: F#m | C#m7 | F#m | C#m7 |

| F#m | C#m7 | A | B :‖ B ‖

201

Velvet

Words & Music by
Robbie Furze & Milo Cordell

A   F#m   D   E5   C#m

⑥ = D♭   ③ = G♭
⑤ = A♭   ② = B♭
④ = D♭   ① = E♭

Intro
| A | A | A | A | F#m |
| F#m | D | D | A | A ‖

Verse 1

A
Seen it in my hands, burning my heart,
        F#m
Seen it in my past, back in my home,
        D
It doesn't make sense to see her again,
     A
I don't   know.

Verse 2

A
I felt it for some time, am I not at all,
        F#m
Poison in my head, gotta love her.
         D
I'm not looking for love, but it's hard to resist,
      A
I don't re - call being this dead.

Link 1
| A | A | F#m | F#m |
| D | D | A | A ‖

Verse 3

A
She's the only one, that's the best I had,
        F#m
I found her in a dream looking for me.

cont.

                 D
This heart's on fire, I'll bring myself

    A
Up to four and down again.

Link 2

| E⁵ | E⁵ | C♯m | C♯m | |
| A | A | E⁵ | E⁵ | ‖ |

Bridge

E⁵   **C♯m**
These arms are mine, don't mind who they own,

                        A
So should I maybe just leave love a - lone?

                         E⁵
You call out my name for the love you need,

But you won't find in me.

E⁵   **C♯m**
These arms are mine, don't mind who they own,

                       A
You're made for me and I'll leave love a - lone.

                         E⁵
You call out my name for the love you need,

But you won't find in me.

Verse 4

(E⁵)   **A**
Seen it in my hands, burning my heart,

              F♯m
I found her in a dream, looking for me.

            D
Doesn't make sense to see her again,

      A
I don't   know.

Verse 5

      A
I can see the end of what I've begun,

          F♯m
A tale of love, come and gone.

            D
And now my love, no promises,

        A
I won't go falling in love.

Outro

| A | A | A | A | ‖ |

Wake Up The Nation

Words by Paul Weller
Music by Paul Weller & Simon Dine

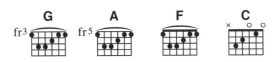

Intro | G | G | G | G ‖

Verse 1
G
Fish from the paper, fresh from the sea,

The cracks in the pavement, the city in siege.

I don't know where to escape it or who to believe.
      A
I can't find an opinion that ain't on its knees,
F   **C**   **G**
Scratching around in a second hand gown when you shouldn't be.

Chorus 1
G
We're going to wake up the nation, don't be no drag,

Shake up the station and out of their hands.

We're going to wake up the nation, don't be no drag,

Shake up the station and out of their hands.
      A
Nowhere to be,
      F   **C**
Nowhere to bleed.

Link 1 | G | G | G | G   ‖

Verse 2
G
Get your face out the Facebook and turn off your phone,

The death of the post box, nowhere feels home,
F   C   G
Scratching around in a second hand gown when you shouldn't be.

Bridge
G
  Shaking it out,

Shaking it out.
A
  Nowhere to be,
F   C   G
  Nowhere to bleed.

Chorus 2
         G
‖: We're going to wake up the nation, don't be no drag,

Shake up the station and out of their hands.

We're going to wake up the nation, don't be no drag,

Shake up the station and out of their hands. :‖ *Repeat to fade*

Wheels

Words & Music by
David Grohl, Chris Shiflett,
Nate Mendel & Taylor Hawkins

C   G   Em   D

Capo second fret

Intro   ‖: C | G | Em | D :‖

Verse 1
C   G   Em D
I know what you're thinking,
C   G   Em D
We were going down.
C   G   Em D
I could feel us sinking,
C   G   Em D
But then I came a - round.

Verse 2
C   G   Em D
And everyone I've loved before
C   G   Em D
Flashed before my eyes,
C   G   Em D
And nothing mattered anymore,
C   G   Em D
I looked into the sky.

Pre-chorus 1
(D)   C   G
Well, I wanted something better man,
Em   D
I wished for something new.
C   G
And I wanted something beautiful,
Em   D
I wished for something true.
C   G
Been looking for a reason man,
Em   D
Something to lose.

Chorus 1
    (D)   **C**   **G**   **Em**   **D**
When the wheels come down, (When the wheels come down)
           C   **G**   **Em**   **D**
When the wheels touch ground, (When the wheels touch ground)
             C   **G**   **Em**   **D**
And you feel like it's all ov - er, there's an - other round for you,
           C   **G**   **Em**   **D**
When the wheels come down. (When the wheels come down)

Link | **C** | **G** | **Em** | **D**   ‖

Verse 3
    C   **G** **Em D**
I know your head is spin - ning,
    C   **G**   **Em D**
Broken hearts will mend.
    C   **G**   **Em D**
This is our be - ginning
    C   **G**   **Em D**
Coming to an end.

Pre-chorus 2
    (D)   **C**   **G**
Well, you wanted something better man,
        Em   **D**
You wished for something new.
           C   **G**
Well, you wanted something beautiful,
Em   **D**
Wished for something true.
        C   **G**
Been looking for a reason man,
Em   **D**
Something to lose.

Chorus 2   As Chorus 1

Instrumental ‖: **C** | **G** | **Em** | **D**   :‖ *Play 6 times*

Chorus 3   As Chorus 1

Chorus 4   As Chorus 1

Outro | **C** | **G** | **Em** | **D**   ‖

Wild Young Hearts

Words & Music by
Shingai Shoniwa, Jamie Morrison,
Daniel Smith & John Fortis

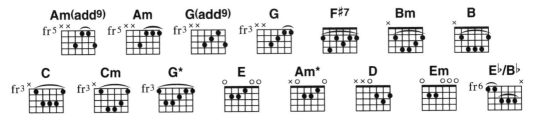

Tune guitar down a semitone

Intro

Am(add9) Am Am(add9) Am
La la   la,   la la   la,

G(add9) G
La la   la, la la la la la la,

Am(add9) Am Am(add9) Am
La la   la,   la la   la,

G(add9) G
La la   la.

Verse 1

(G)   Am(add9) Am
And while the city   sleeps

Am(add9) Am   G(add9) G
I won't   weep because I didn't   keep

G(add9)   G   Am(add9) Am   Am(add9) Am
My boy - friend and the summer's end is here   again

          G(add9) G
And the leaves   are golden

          F#7   Bm   B
Under the grand silver birch tree.

Verse 2

(B)   Am(add9) Am
While we're thinking 'bout the people we meet,

Am(add9) Am G(add9)   G   G(add9) G
Dancing   feet, wasters on the cover of a maga - zine.

A(add9)   Am   Am(add9)   Am
People you've kissed, people you lost

          G(add9) G
And the ones that you might not

          F#7   Bm   B
Ever re - member, what's the use?

Chorus 1

   C   Cm
   I'm not what I was last summer,

G*   E
Not who I was in the spring.

C
Tell me, tell me, tell me when will we learn,

   Cm
We love it and we leave it and we watch it burn.

G*   E
Damn these wild young hearts.

Am*   D   Cm   G*
Damn these wild young hearts.

Verse 3

(G)   Am(add⁹) Am   Am(add⁹) Am
Now that the city's   a - wake, my heart aches,

        G(add⁹)   G   G(add⁹)   G
Oh, what a silly mis - take it seems I've made.

     A(add⁹)   Am   Am(add⁹) Am
You left your keys und - er my   bed,

     G(add⁹)   G
Left a thumping in my head,

        F♯7   Bm
I would say sorry, what's the use?

Chorus 2

B   C   Cm
'Cause, I'm   not what I was last Sep - tember,

   G*   E
And I don't wear the same robes in May.

   C
We know we shouldn't do it but we do it anyway,

   Cm
We know we might regret it but it seemed okay.

G*   E
  Damn these wild young hearts.

Am*   D   Bm   Em
Damn these wild young hearts.___

Am*   D   Cm   G*
Damn these wild young hearts.

Link

Am(add9)   Am   Am(add9)   Am
La la   la, la la   la,

G(add9)   G
La la   la, la la la la la la,

Am(add9)   Am   Am(add9)   Am
La la   la, la la   la,

G(add9)   G
La la   la.

Bridge

(G)   B
If now is for - ever then what's to prove,

Chorus 3

(B)   C   Cm
'Cause it   won't be the same next summer

    G*   **E**
And I guess I'll see you in the spring.

             C
Somebody tell me, tell me, tell me, when will I learn

 Cm
I love it and I leave it and I watch it burn.

G*   **E**
Damn this wild young heart,

       Am*   **D**   **Bm   Em**
I told you damn this wild young heart.____

Am*   **D**
Damn this wild young,

Bm   **Em**
Tell me, tell me, tell me when will I learn,

Am*   **D**   **E♭/B♭**   **G**
Damn this wild young heart.

210

Witchcraft

Words & Music by
Rob Swire & Gareth McGrillen

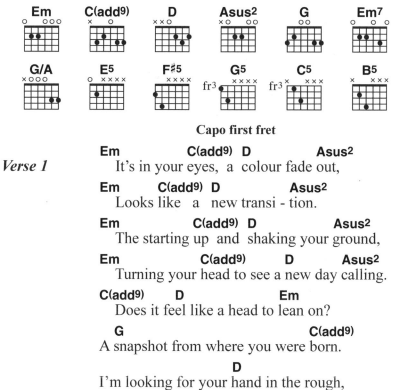

Capo first fret

Verse 1

```
       Em            C(add9) D         Asus2
        It's in your eyes, a  colour fade out,
       Em     C(add9) D           Asus2
        Looks like  a  new transi - tion.
       Em              C(add9) D         Asus2
        The starting up  and  shaking your ground,
       Em            C(add9)        D         Asus2
        Turning your head to see a new day calling.
     C(add9)      D              Em
        Does it feel like a head to lean on?
      G                           C(add9)
     A snapshot from where you were born.
                          D
     I'm looking for your hand in the rough,
            Em7             G/F#
     You're caught in the wire,
      G            G/A     (Em)
        Well, I'll lift you out.
```

Instrumental 1

```
‖: Em        | C(add9)    | D        | Asus2      :‖ Play 4 times

   | E5       | E5 F#5 G5 | E5       | C5 B5 A5 B5 G5 |

   | E5       | E5 F#5 G5 | E5       | E5 C5 B5 G5 |

   | E5       | E5 F#5 G5 | E5       | C5 B5 A5 B5 G5 |

   | E5       | E5 F#5 G5 | Em       | D           ‖
```

Verse 2

Em   **C(add9)**
Leading on the action,

D   **Asus2**
Caught in a cellphone's rays.

Em   **C(add9)**
Bleeding on a sofa,

D   **Asus2**
Staring at the wayside.

      Em   **C(add9)**
He's coming and she knows it,

D   **Asus2**
Even though she knows why.

Em7   **G/F♯**
Footsteps in the hallway,

 G   **G/A**
Girl you haven't got time.

Chorus 1

(G/A)   **Em** **C(add9)** **D**
You gotta get out,

Asus2   **Em** **C(add9)** **D**
  Go far a - way.

Asus2   **Em** **C(add9)** **D**
   You gotta get out,

Asus2   **Em** **C(add9)** **D** **Asus2**
Go far a - way.

Instrumental 2 | **E5** | **E5** **F♯5** **G5** | **E5** | **C5** **B5** **A5** **B5** **G5** |

                  | **E5** | **E5** **F♯5** **G5** | **E5** | **E5** **C5** **B5** **G5** |

                  | **E5** | **E5** **F♯5** **G5** | **E5** | **C5** **B5** **A5** **B5** **G5** |

                  | **E5** | **E5** **F♯5** **G5** | **Em** | **D**   ‖

Verse 3

Em   C(add9)
Darkness in the bedroom,

D   Asus2
Maybe she is resting up.

Em   C(add9)
Maybe she was out late,

D   Asus2
Just come back from the club.

 Em   C(add9)
I can't hear her breathing,

D   Asus2
Something doesn't seem right.

Em7   G/F♯
Killer in the hallway,

       G   G/A
We're living in a set time.

Chorus 2

(G/A)   Em C(add9) D
We gotta get out,

Asus2   Em C(add9) D
Go far a - way.

Asus2   Em C(add9) D
  We gotta get out,

Asus2   Em C(add9) D Asus2
Go far a - way.

Outro

‖: E5	E5 F♯5 G5	E5		C5 B5 A5 B5 G5
E5	E5 F♯5 G5	E5		E5 C5 B5 G5
E5	E5 F♯5 G5	E5		C5 B5 A5 B5 G5
E5	E5 F♯5 G5	Em		D	:‖ Em	

213

M.I.A.

XXXO

Words & Music by
Maya Arulpragasam, Charles Smith & Cherry Byron-Withers

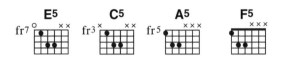

Intro | E⁵ | E⁵ | E⁵ | E⁵   ‖

Verse 1

E⁵   C⁵
Time after time you been copping mine,
      A⁵   F⁵
But can I have a good time at yours tonight.
E⁵   C⁵
'Cause every time we try to get close
A⁵   F⁵
There is always something big I'm thinking about.

Pre-chorus 1

E⁵
You want me,

XXXO, XXXO,

You want me,

XXXO, XXXO,

You want me,

XXXO, XXXO,

You want me,

XXXO,

You want me,

XXXO.

Chorus 1

E5   C5
You want me be somebody who I'm really not.

                A5   F5
You want me be somebody who I'm really not.

E5   C5
You want me be somebody who I'm really not.

                A5   F5
You want me be somebody who I'm really not.

Verse 2

           E5   C5
A knock at the door and then we hit the floor,

      A5   F5
And all I know is you leave me wanting more.

E5   C5
I don't let it show, but I think you know,

             A5   F5
'Cause you tweeting me like Tweety Bird on your iPhone.

Pre-chorus 2   As Pre-chorus 1

Chorus 2   As Chorus 1

Verse 3

E5
Upload your photo, see below,

If you see what you like you can download and store.

We can find ways to expand what you know,

I can be the actress, you be Tarantino.

216

Pre-chorus 3

E5
You want me,

        C5
XXXO, XXXO,

You want me,

A5   **F5**
XXXO, XXXO,

You want me,

E5   **C5**
XXXO, XXXO,

You want me,

A5
XXXO,

You want me,

F5
XXXO.

Chorus 3

E5   **C5**
You want me be somebody who I'm really not.

             A5   **F5**
You want me be somebody who I'm really not.

E5   **C5**
You want me be somebody who I'm really not.

             A5   **F5**
You want me be somebody who I'm really not.

             E5 **C5**
You want me be,

             A5 **F5**
You want me.

             E5 **C5**
You want me be,

             A5 **F5** **E5**
You want me.

You Overdid It Doll

Words & Music by
Liam Fray

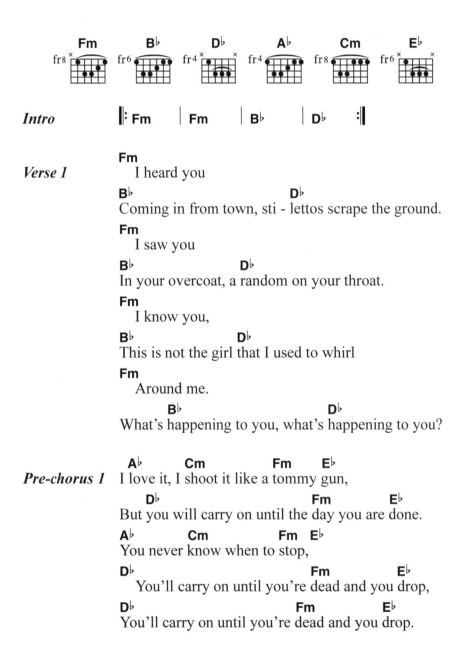

Intro   ‖: Fm | Fm | B♭ | D♭ :‖

Verse 1

Fm
  I heard you
B♭   D♭
Coming in from town, sti - lettos scrape the ground.
Fm
  I saw you
B♭   D♭
In your overcoat, a random on your throat.
Fm
  I know you,
B♭   D♭
This is not the girl that I used to whirl
Fm
  Around me.
    B♭   D♭
What's happening to you, what's happening to you?

Pre-chorus 1

A♭   Cm   Fm   E♭
I love it, I shoot it like a tommy gun,
    D♭   Fm   E♭
But you will carry on until the day you are done.
A♭   Cm   Fm   E♭
You never know when to stop,
D♭   Fm   E♭
  You'll carry on until you're dead and you drop,
D♭   Fm   E♭
You'll carry on until you're dead and you drop.

Chorus 1

Fm
You overdid it doll, you overdid it doll,
B♭   D♭
You overdid it doll,   you overdid it doll.
Fm
You overdid it doll, you overdid it doll,
B♭   D♭
You overdid it doll,   you overdid it doll.

Link 1 | Fm | Fm | B♭ | D♭   ‖

Verse 2

Fm
Your teeth are starting to go,
B♭   D♭
Five nights a week is starting to show.
Fm
Dark rims around your eyes,
   B♭   D♭
Are fashionable until somebody dies.
Fm
This pace, a little too fast,
    B♭   D♭
You're a space cadet dressed in fibreglass.
          Fm
You're gonna shatter, it's not too late to undo,
   B♭   D♭
Put the fiddle down, the taming of the shrew.

Pre-chorus 2   As Pre-chorus 1

Chorus 2   As Chorus 1

Guitar solo ‖: Fm | Fm | B♭ | D♭ :‖

Bridge

      A♭   Cm   Fm E♭

You will never know when to stop,

      D♭   Fm   E♭

  You'll carry on until you're dead and you drop,

      D♭   Fm   E♭

You'll carry on until you're dead and you drop.

Pre-chorus 3

      A♭   Cm   Fm   E♭

I love it, I shoot it like a tommy gun,

       D♭   Fm   E♭

But you will carry on until the day you are done,

      D♭   Fm   E♭

You will carry on until the day you are done.

Chorus 3   As Chorus 1

Outro   ‖: Fm | Fm | B♭ | D♭ :‖ *Repeat to fade*

Zebra

Words & Music by
Victoria Legrand & Alex Scally

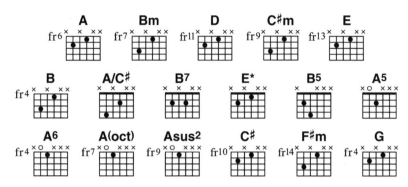

Tune guitar down a semitone

(Chord names reflect simplified harmony)

Intro | A | Bm | D C#m Bm | A |

| A | Bm | D C#m Bm | A   C#m |

| D | C#m | E | A |

| Bm | Bm   A | B A/C# B7 | B7 E* B5 |

| A5   A6 | A(oct) Asus2 ‖

| A | Bm | D C#m Bm | A |
Ah,_____   Ah,_____

| A | Bm | D C#m Bm | A   C#m |
Ah,_____   Ah,_____

| D | C#m | E | A |
Ah,_____

| Bm | Bm   A | B A/C# B7 | B7 E* B5 |
Ah,_____

| A5   A6 | A(oct) Asus2 ‖

Verse 1

```
        A                   Bm  D  C#m    Bm   A
        You know you're gold, you    don't got to worry none,

        A      Bm  D   C#m Bm A   C#m
        Oasis child, born and so___ wild.

        D      C#m      E            A
        Don't I know you better than the rest?

        Bm        A    B  A/C# B7     E*    B5    A5    A6 A(oct) Asus2
        All decep - tion, all      decep - tion from you.
```

Verse 2

```
        A                   Bm D C#m  Bm  A
        Your love's a stag in the white   sand,

        A                Bm   D    C#m Bm    A    C#m
        Wilderness for miles, eyes so  mild and wise.

        D      C#m      E            A
        Don't I know you better than the rest?

        Bm        A    B  A/C# B7     E*    B5    A5    A6 A(oct) Asus2
        All decep - tion, all      decep - tion from you.
```

Chorus 1

```
        A     C#      D   F#m      E     C#m
        Any way you run,    you run before us,

        Bm              E*    G      A/C#   E*
        Black and white horse arching among us.

        A     C#      D   F#m      E     C#m
        Any way you run,    you run before us,

        Bm              E*    G      A/C#   E*
        Black and white horse arching among us.
```

Link 1

```
        | A          | A          | A          | A          ||
```

Verse 3

```
        A                   Bm D C#m  Bm  A
        Your love's a stag in the white   sand,

        A      Bm  D   C#m Bm A   C#m
        Oasis child born into  a    man.

        D      C#m      E            A
        Don't I know you better than the rest?

        Bm        A    B  A/C# B7     E*    B5    A5    A6 A(oct) Asus2
        All decep - tion, all      decep - tion from you.
```

Verse 4

```
        A              Bm    D    C♯m   Bm    A
        Wilderness for miles, eyes so mild and wise,

        A      Bm    D    C♯m   Bm  A    C♯m
        Oasis child, born and so___ wild.

        D        C♯m      E              A
        Don't I know you better than the rest?

        Bm       A    B   A/C♯  B7      E*   B5   A5   A6  A(oct)  A6  A5
        All decep - tion, all      decep - tion from you.
```

Chorus 2   As Chorus 1

Chorus 3   As Chorus 1

Outro

```
| A    C♯ | D       | F♯m    E | C♯m      |

| Bm      | E*      | G    A/C♯ | E*       |

| A    C♯ | D       | F♯m    E | C♯m      |

| Bm      | E*      | G    A/C♯ | E*       |

| E*      | E*      | E*       | A       ‖
```

Relative Tuning

The guitar can be tuned with the aid of pitch pipes or dedicated electronic guitar tuners which are available through your local music dealer. If you do not have a tuning device, you can use relative tuning. Estimate the pitch of the 6th string as near as possible to E or at least a comfortable pitch (not too high, as you might break other strings in tuning up). Then, while checking the various positions on the diagram, place a finger from your left hand on the:

5th fret of the E or 6th string and **tune the open A** (or 5th string) to the note (A)

5th fret of the A or 5th string and **tune the open D** (or 4th string) to the note (D)

5th fret of the D or 4th string and **tune the open G** (or 3rd string) to the note (G)

4th fret of the G or 3rd string and **tune the open B** (or 2nd string) to the note (B)

5th fret of the B or 2nd string and **tune the open E** (or 1st string) to the note (E)

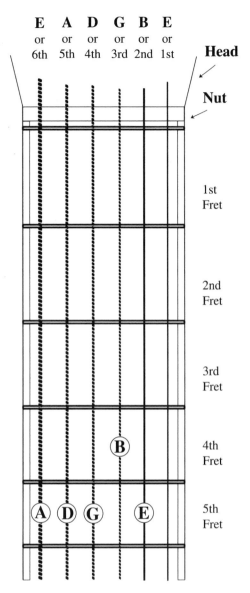

Reading Chord Boxes

Chord boxes are diagrams of the guitar neck viewed head upwards, face on as illustrated. The top horizontal line is the nut, unless a higher fret number is indicated, the others are the frets.

The vertical lines are the strings, starting from E (or 6th) on the left to E (or 1st) on the right.

The black dots indicate where to place your fingers.

Strings marked with an O are played open, not fretted. Strings marked with an X should not be played.

The curved bracket indicates a 'barre' - hold down the strings under the bracket with your first finger, using your other fingers to fret the remaining notes.

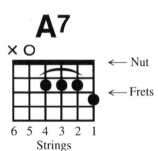